GW00385120

URGENT

what would you do if this happened to you?

RANDOM HOUSE AUSTRALIA

Random House Australia Pty Ltd
20 Alfred Street, Milsons Point, NSW 2061
http://www.randomhouse.com.au

Sydney   New York   Toronto
London   Auckland   Johannesburg

First published by Random House Australia 2003

National Library of Australia
Cataloguing-in-Publication Data

Urgent.

For secondary school students.
ISBN 1 74051 904 3.

1. Aborigines, Australian - Fiction. 2. Aborigines,
Australian - Removal - Fiction.

A823.4

Cover and internal design by Shayne Lacy
Cover image by Stefanie Driscoll
Printed and bound by Griffin Press, Netley, South Australia

The stories in the book are the same for many of our people. The wider community does not understand how the current younger generation have been affected by the recent history of the stolen generation. One of the glaringly obvious ways to help our people is to keep our young people at school. This book will help raise awareness of young Aboriginal issues.
Mrs Lyn McInnes, Chair, Wathaurong Aboriginal Cooperative

Health does not simply mean the physical wellbeing of the individual but refers to social, emotional and cultural wellbeing. This remarkable compilation, Urgent, *allows each of us to take a step upon our own journey towards coming to terms with the inequalities facing Indigenous Australians. It is an incredible chronicle of hope, inspiration and, above all, of forgiveness.*
Professor Michael Kidd, President, Royal Australian College of General Practitioners

This rich and emotionally moving book captures the struggle for identity, the awful nature of racism and injustice, and the importance of feeling connected to family and community. Based upon the experiences of three Indigenous young women with a shared but unknown father, Urgent *asks, 'How would this feel if this were done to me?' It conveys a profound and universal message of understanding and forgiveness.*
Associate Professor David Bennett AO, Head, NSW Centre for the Advancement of Adolescent Health

There is nothing more important in advancing our understanding of mental health issues than personal accounts of the costs, lost opportunities and life-changing experiences that accompany them. This book provides one such account. Hopefully it will cause people to stop, rethink their attitudes and consider how important the loss of families and communities is to us all.
Professor Ian Hickie, Chief Executive Officer, beyond blue, National Depression Initiative

ear Juliet,

I want to tell you about The Dandelion Theory of Life. The jagged line represents the highs and lows of a life. The peaks is a pleasing ascent from a pleasing ascent. The emotion. Each peak is a pleasing ascent into a period of contentment. The discomfort and into a period of 'line of middle-most discomfort and into the 'line of middle-most that a point sinks below the 'line of middle-most emotion. Life that a point sinks below the 'negative emotion. As we never the higher the degree of 'negative emotion. Therefore the higher the degree of in a cycle, as we never continue in a cycle, as we never continue into to another. Therefore woods continue into to another.
into to another. what like

for Louis

As a boy growing up in Darwin, I heard very little racism and saw no poverty or violence amongst the Aboriginal people, yet I spent much of my childhood living with them. I visited numerous outstations across Arnhem Land in a tiny single-prop aeroplane with my mum and my brother. My mum worked for the Northern Land Council as secretary to Galarrwuy Yunupingu, the chairman, and when he visited outstations my brother and I were welcome to go along. We would land on an old gravel airstrip, then taxi across the soft bulldust to a large corrugated iron shed with a torn and battered windsock. Looking out the window, I would always recognise the familiar sight, a sight I believe to be true Territorian country – red dust, white eucalypt trees with burnt bases, and crowns with dazzling bright green foliage. As the plane's propeller clunked off and the swirling dust settled, out from the shed and nearby scrub would run throngs of little black faces with pearly white teeth in tiny black and navy-blue stubby shorts. I loved this place, a place I knew was home… We had no names for the Aboriginal children, no need. My brother and I would be whisked away by the drove of Aboriginal kids to go fishing, bark painting and to be covered in ochre like a blank white canvas. I never quite understood why we went to these outstations with Mum and Galarrwuy, or even questioned why my mum worked for a black man. I just knew that if Mum was going bush and we were invited, adventures would always be on the cards, and with the Aboriginal kids we'd always be safe. We ate well: fish, crabs, yams and pig. There was no sign of alcoholism, drugs and violence. Sure the adults drank beer and occasionally got drunk – I even remember an elder who got a little tipsy one night and promised he would make me a spear…it never happened…but I suppose it was better that a six-year-old not be armed with a three-pronged fishing spear! The children always had distended bellies, not from malnutrition but from always being full.

One day my family flew to Nhulunbuy, with my beloved Scottish pop who had never experienced the Aboriginal way of life. It was just as much of an adventure for an old man who had seen war, prisoner camps and poverty, as it was for us two little boys. Neither my brother nor I knew why we were going, we just knew that we were staying on our favourite beach, Ski Beach, and where there's a beach there's fishing! Galarrwuy would take his spear down to the water's edge and catch us some crabs and fish for bait. Our silly adventurous minds would even make us gather flimsy long sticks, which we would use to pole-vault onto distant sandbars as deadly box jellyfish cruised transparently underneath. Two adventurous white boys in a black people's land…we fitted in easily.

I will forever remember the day when both my brother and I became more than just close white friends of the Yunupingus; we became part of their family. Craig and I didn't know it, however, we had travelled to Nhulunbuy for a very special ceremony of the Gumatj Clan (the tribe of the Yunupingus) to honour Galarrwuy's father, who had recently passed away. We arrived at the beach to see hundreds of people cooking, dressing in ceremonial dress and singing. Out across the sea a small boat could be seen slowly making its way to a small makeshift boat ramp just 100 metres away. As the boat came closer I saw an enormous crocodile lying in the boat, mouth agape as if it were basking. Although I thought this sight was strange, everyone around me looked on seriously, so I assumed it was part of the ceremony. As the boat neared the shore a dozen or so Aboriginal men, including Galarrwuy, started chanting, singing and gesturing with spears and dilly bags. Holding the dilly bags in their mouths, like a crocodile would its prey, they thumped their feet hard into the ground as they slowly made their way to the men now out of the boat and holding onto a pontoon which cradled the enormous crocodile. I will never forget the body-penetrating sounds of the Aboriginal men chanting, 'Whoop hah, whoop hah, whoop he-i, whoop he-ii!', as they ran across the 100-metre stretch thumping their bare feet into solid scorching ground. While all of this was going on, the young Aboriginal boys were being covered from head to foot in white clay by a pair of gigantic Aboriginal elder

7

women. Without even questioning why we were there, both women let out a quiet giggle, grabbed my brother and me, took off our t-shirts, and began to cover us in clay. Imagine these two ghostly apparitions marching off among a sea of black bodies to stand around a crocodile encircled by fire. The women crowded around the crocodile and began to cry and wail. It was an emotional time, and although I could not understand why the women were crying over a massive crocodile, I knew deep down that this was a very special animal to them. I now know that the crocodile is the totem of the Gumatj Clan and the ceremony was to release Galarrwuy's fathers' spirit from the slain crocodile. On that day, my brother and I received tribal names from Galarrwuy's sisters. Mine was Luwatpuy, after 'a place near Bryane Bryane' – an outstation of the Gumatj Clan.

Since leaving Darwin, I have learned more about my time as a child with the Aboriginal people. I understand now that my mum was working for Land Rights. I have also learned that the ceremonies my family attended were not tourist corroborees, but strong family gatherings to mourn the dead, celebrate achievements like Galarrwuy's Order of Australia, and to revel in the initiation of young men into manhood. I have yet to fully realise the intense spiritual and emotional experiences I had as a child, as at the time it was simply all a big adventure.

In 2002, I travelled the country as Young Australian of the Year, and I have visited many places, seen many things, and talked to people who have a vested interest in the wellbeing of the Australian Aboriginal people. In particular, I have been constantly reminded of the efforts of two other Australians of the Year, Galarrwuy and Mandawuy Yunupingu. I have also met many people who wouldn't think twice about making racial slurs against Aboriginal people, and freely comment upon the millions of dollars 'wasted on a bunch of people who don't even want to look after themselves'. If this is indeed the situation, then as a boy I must have experienced an Aboriginal utopia. Possibly more likely, the problems of the world were kept away from the Aboriginal children (and my brother and me), allowing them (and us) the chance to grow up in a culture full of love, compassion and understanding. I know that for some of my Aboriginal friends in the Northern Territory, drugs, alcohol and violence have become a major part of their adult lives.

Reading *Urgent* has given me yet another perspective on current feelings, emotions and problems facing Aboriginal Australians today, especially youth. These problems should never have arisen, as I have experienced life in an Aboriginal land where the heart is still strong and the people still united. My Aboriginal utopia may not exist any more in real terms, but I am sure it does in people's hearts. The trick is to bring these feelings back and give Aboriginal people the understanding, compassion and acceptance that they gave me, a six-year-old white boy of Scottish ancestry. It is obvious from Dr Fitzgerald's experiences with Aboriginal people that the simple act of communication is the greatest way to break down the barriers imposed over 200 years of colonisation. Non-Aboriginal Australians need to acknowledge the barriers that exist and help Aboriginal Australians rediscover their utopia, embedded deep within their hearts and land. Take it from a six-year-old white boy adopted into an Aboriginal family: 'Where the fishin' is good, friends are forever'.

Luwatpuy (a.k.a. Scott Hocknull)
Young Australian of the Year 2002
Assistant Curator, Palaeontology, Vertebrate Palaeontologist,
Queensland Museum

URGENT

Contributors

Urgent is a collaborative work of fiction based on true stories and a project of the Wathaurong Aboriginal Cooperative. All profits from the sale of this book go to Wathaurong.

Authors

Joleen Ryan
Julia Torpey
Megan Torpey
Tegan Watson

Zac Brennan – poetry (pp 41, 58, 66, 81, 84), artwork (pp 29, 39, 59, 166, 168)

Additional material: Renne Boulton, Shirahan Brown, Chloe Chandler (pp 120–123), Elise Davey (pp 163), Edwina Dethridge (pp 124, 136, 154), Leah Eddy (pp 96, 145), Alinta Edwards, Stephen Edwards, Fallon Forbes (pp 113, 150), Kristi Grbin (pp 34–36), Kristy Hill (p 49), Justin Hollander, Louis Jasek (pp 74, 106), Hanh Le (pp 134, 135), Richard McKinnon, Veronica Milsom (p 24), Leanne Rowe (pp 18–21), Jayde Secombe, Shannon Secombe, Felicity Sherwell (pp 119, 128–129, 148), Sarah Sinclair, Tony Talevski (photo p 16), Mark Torpey (p 92), Kate Torpey (p 98)

Photography and Artwork

Cover: Stefanie Driscoll

Other: Stefanie Driscoll (pp 25, 30, 40, 50, 69, 77, 85, 91, 93, 104, 117, 130, 144, 147, 151, 152, 157, 162,), Frances Farnan (pp 61, 75, 88), Alison King (pp 33, 57, 67, 80, 108, 118, 125, 143, 161), Martin Kumnick (p 97), Joleen Ryan (p 47), Tegan Watson (p 137)

Coordinator/Editor: Dr Leanne Rowe

Design: Shayne Lacy (www.mspace.com.au)

The authors wish to thank Wathaurong Aboriginal Cooperative, Mrs Lyn McInnes, Mrs Patricia Clarke, Mrs Kerry McCarthy, Ms Kathy Travis, Mr Scott Hocknull, Mr Bruce Pascoe, Sharon and Jim Stynes and Yelda Adal (The Reach Foundation). We are also indebted to The Hon. Malcolm Fraser (pp 138–139), The Hon. Paul Keating (pp 159), Professor Robert Manne (p 158), Mr George Megalogenis (pp 110–112), and Mr Ron Tandberg (pp 107) for permission to use their work in the book.
Other acknowledgements are given in the Afterword on p 170.

Contents

1: The Dandelion Theory   15
2: Contact   27
3: Meeting   63
4: Reaction   83
5: The Secret   127

1: The Dandelion Theory

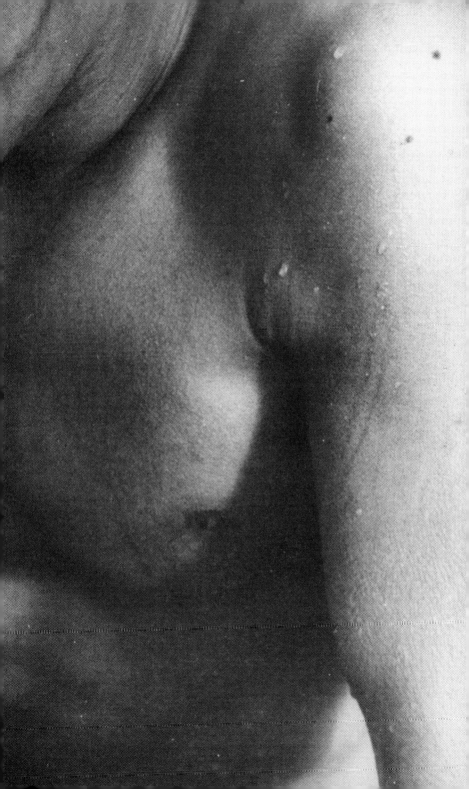

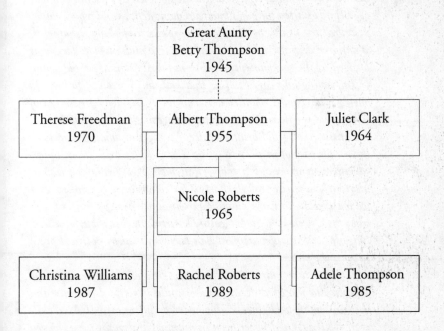

Dear Reader,

The more I work in Aboriginal health as a doctor, the less I am inclined to comment on this complex, delicate issue for fear of saying something politically incorrect. However, I need to unburden my feelings of being overwhelmed while working for a few months at an Aboriginal community-controlled health service in Northern Queensland. What started as an idea to help finance some long-service leave after 10 years in my own practice in Victoria became an inspiring, emotional experience, which has led to personal change.

Before I started the job, I had read many articles and reports which described the health of Aboriginal people as 'appalling', 'shameful', 'a national disgrace'. I had assumed that with millions of dollars being pledged by the government, conditions for Aboriginal people would be improving and could not be that bad, but I resolved to keep an open mind. Now I wonder why Australia's shameful treatment of Aboriginal people is not on the front page of every newspaper.

At the Aboriginal health service, I was given what seemed to be the simple task of helping to set up a 'well kids' clinic' in an isolated settlement on the outskirts of a rural town. I was to promote immunisation and check growth charts. Our community-controlled service wanted me to work alongside community health services funded by the Queensland State Health Department, even though the relationship with the department had been strained by political problems in the past.

I noted that many babies and children were undernourished. Women did not breastfeed; families could not afford formula and they commonly fed babies adult powdered milk or cordial. Most children of all ages had never been immunised and many were covered in scabies and impetigo, including a three-week-old baby.

A five-month-old baby presenting for routine immunisation at our clinic was delirious with meningitis. His 20-year-old mother and her aggressive partner refused to take him to hospital because their other two children had died there of cot death and during labour. I saw another two-year-old with congenital heart disease and pneumonia. She died in hospital one week later. I had known that Aboriginal babies were twice as likely to die as non-Aboriginal

18

babies, but I could not believe that their general health could be so appalling.

In the first few weeks, the mothers replied to my questions with one-word answers and downcast eyes, sometimes just walking away to spit filthy phlegm through broken flyscreens or to slap their toddlers. The children played with blue marbles in their mouths while running about wildly with my medical equipment or chasing dogs out of the clinic.

Aunties and grandmothers laughed riotously as each child cried with their immunisation. Amidst the chaos and the dancing of eyes, I found it difficult to work out which child belonged to which parent. They all seemed to belong to everyone. Although it would have been easy to assume that this represented a situation of gross child neglect, it seemed that it was actually a sad acceptance that illness and postnatal depression were a normal part of everyday Aboriginal life experience.

Although many of the women were unwell, they hesitated to talk about themselves, always putting the needs of the children before their own. As she held her sick granddaughter, one 40-year-old woman apologised for taking up my time as she mentioned 24 hours of right-sided numbness. She had undiagnosed severe high blood pressure and had had a stroke. She had been too busy looking after her children and grandchildren to walk an hour to the town doctor.

I entertained the idea of a questionnaire to assess postnatal depression or self-esteem, but then wondered what I would do with significant results. Discrimination, crowded housing, lack of resources and money, domestic violence and poor nutrition made it difficult to think of positive strategies.

As the weeks went by, the women seemed to engage me with their eyes and discussed their problems spontaneously. I felt the importance of developing a trusting relationship. The more I saw of how people lived in such difficult circumstances, the more I admired their strength. I often wondered how long it would be before I turned to alcohol or the TAB if I lived with their problems.

My second task was to attend a 'well women's clinic' to help screen for cervical cancer (the incidence of which is 17 times that of the non-Aboriginal population). Complex medical problems such as diabetes, heart disease, infections and chronic pain were common, but the women wanted to talk about their emotional difficulties. I searched for the words to say to a 25-year-old who had three children in foster care and whose husband was in jail for domestic violence, when she opened the consultation with the statement: 'Four boys forced sex on me when I was 14 and I have never told anyone.' We sat in silence for a while, both struggling with the enormity of this terrible secret.

When I saw another woman for what appeared to be a routine pap smear, she mentioned out of the blue that she felt like killing herself. Many women were under stress from domestic violence, sexual abuse, caring for ill and dying relatives (the average life expectancy is about 55 years), brothers and sisters, and their own children.

As I drove to work, I often saw homeless Aboriginal people living in the parks, arguing and drinking alcohol. The 'park people' sometimes featured on the front page of the local newspaper because of concerns that their presence was affecting the tourist dollar, and this reflected the non-Aboriginal, hardened reaction to the problem. It was difficult to explain to my six-year-old son why these people lived in public toilet blocks. My children continue to be very upset that the park people have nowhere to go at night or when it rains, and that when they change their clothes in the park, people might see their bottoms.

I feel a great need to talk about what I have seen, but few people seem to want to listen. While many people with little knowledge of Aboriginal health don't particularly care about my experiences, others ask the same questions: 'Why did you leave your comfortable practice to work in a low-status job?'; 'Why have millions of dollars been poured into Aboriginal health when it is hopeless due to their lack of motivation and alcoholism?'; 'How did you stand the smell?'

I can only answer that I have learnt a great deal and that my social conscience has been wakened. Stereotyping and generalisations are unjust, extremely damaging, and a barrier to Aboriginal people accessing available health services. For example, many Aboriginal people were insulted that the first question they were asked when they attended the local hospital was about their alcohol intake (although available evidence suggests that 40 per cent of Aboriginal people are teetotallers compared to less than 30 per cent of non-Aboriginal people). This attitude deterred many Aboriginal people from attending the hospital, which meant they often presented late with serious illnesses.

I asked all of my Aboriginal patients where they found the strength to carry on through such difficult circumstances, and their answer was always the same – their hope for their children's future. The only smell I have experienced is the stench of racism. How will we be able to live with our consciences when our own children feel compelled to apologise because our generation allowed yet another generation of Aboriginal children to grow up with chronic illness and poverty? Why do we assume the problems are too hard, too political or someone else's responsibility? I feel as though I am presenting a speech no one is listening to. I have been thinking for a long time about how to best communicate what I have learned to non-Aboriginal people.

Perhaps I can do that best by telling the story of one patient, Albert Thompson. I met many people like Albert. He was stolen from his family at four years of age and was unable to resolve his loss.

One day, I was called to Albert's isolated shack at the end of a bumpy dirt road through a dense rainforest. He was a 37-year-old diabetic man with heart disease and renal failure, and he had been suffering from chest pain. When I arrived, I found him dead, curled up awkwardly on his stretcher bed. As I examined him, a large unopened envelope marked 'URGENT' fell from his arms. While I sat at his table waiting for the police and writing up his medical notes, I noticed Albert's folder of poetry, with one poem written on the morning of his death. I then opened the envelope marked 'URGENT' and I am sending you a copy of the extraordinary contents.

Should I write to his daughters? What would you say to them? What would you do if this happened to you?

Dr Jason Fitzgerald

last touch of the
smooth face, so innocent.
One last glimpse of their
smiles, so true.
laugh, No life.

MR. MRS. MISS	THOMPSON	NAMES	ALBERT	STATUS	D.O.B. 1955
			KOOROWA	PHONE	no
ADDRESS	OLD FOREST LANE				
		MEDICARE NO.			
OCCUPATION/EMPLOYER	UNEMPLOYED	PVTE. INS. no		PENSION NO	

F.H. TAKEN FROM FAMILY AGE 4 FAMILY UNKNOWN EXCEPT FOR AUNTY- BETTY THOMPSON BETTY - DIABETES	S.H. No ALCOHOL left School 15 yrs gifted artist, photographer, poet

P.H. HYPERTENSION, ANGINA DIABETES OBESITY ® BLINDNESS DEPRESSION	IMMUNIZATIONS	ALLERGIES NIL

PROBLEMS	
lives alone lost contact with 3 daughters Socially isolated no transport refuses to attend local hospital due to past experiences of racism poor nutrition highfat	Medications: poor compliance Metformin 500mg tds Tritace 10mg ō tds Nifedipine 20mg ō bd Nitrolingual pump Spray prn.

HEAVY SMOKER
60/DAY

The storm had arrived
Leaving my withered branches fruitless and bare
No soul, No remains.
Just me.

One last touch of the smooth face, so innocent.
One last glimpse of their smiles, so true.
No laugh, No life.
Just me.

A lifetime removed in seconds
A generation in bloom
Nothing left but my bare hands
And me.

The seeds that had fallen have grown,
Unaware of what could have been,
A seed created has drifted, away with the wind,
And me.

A reconstruction of events through my head,
A better solution in hand,
A dream that never subsided,
A dream of my daughters and me.

Albert Thompson
5 April 2003

seeds that
had fallen
have
grown,
unaware of
what could
have been,
a seed
created
has drifted,
away with
the wind

2: Contact

3 April 2003

Mr Albert Thompson
Koorowa
Northern Queensland

Dear Albert,

We only discovered a few months ago that we are sisters and share you as our father. Great Aunty Betty also said that you are very sick. These months have turned our lives around and we initially felt very angry with you because you have never been there for us. But now we want you to understand how important you are to us.

We know about the secret.

At our first meeting, we put together a scrapbook of memories of our lives and stories from our mothers about your life. We need to know that our story means something to you. Please read our book and write back to us.

We feel as though our futures depend on your answer.

With much love from your daughters,

Adele Thompson
Christina Williams
Rachel Roberts

3 January 2003

Ms Adele Thompson
PO Box 128
Bannockburn
Victoria 3331

Dear Adele,

I know that we don't really get along, but we still care about you. We know that you don't want much to do with your Aboriginal background, but I can respect that. Your father, Albert, is dying, Addy. Although he has been in and out of your life, he still loves you.

You have two sisters. Christina Williams is 16 years old and adopted by Sarah Williams. Rachel Roberts is living with her mother, Nicole Roberts. The girls are now living in non-Aboriginal families. Albert wants you to find them and get to know them. He did mention an organisation called Link Up. So you could go through them and try finding them that way.

It's been too long since we last saw you. I heard you finished Year 12. How'd you go? Well, I hope. But no matter how you went, congratulations on finishing your VCE. I'm proud of you. You must think you are a big shot now with you finishing Year 12 and all, hey? Well, at least you're getting somewhere.

Find your sisters, Addy, and get to know them. Say hi to your brother and Juliet for me.

Nukkin ya,
Great Aunty Betty Thompson
Koorowa, Northern Queensland

Dreaming

With these eyes I see a magnificent world,
Of hope, of beauty and goodwill.

With these hands I feel an ancient rock,
The prehistoric ferns and an ongoing stream.

With this nose I smell a scent of history,
A dusty shack and the hint of a bushfire.

With this tongue I taste the sweet blossoms,
The sour fruit and the charred meat.

With these ears I hear the sound of clapping,
The soft singing and the gentle stirring of those forever
gone.

Adele Thompson

5 January 2003

Dear Diary,

All this time and Albert never told me. Sisters? I have sisters? Does Mum know? Perhaps not. After all, Albert walked out on her and started travelling when I was one and a half. Mum must have stayed in touch with Albert's Aunty Betty, for my sake, I suppose.

Two years ago, when I was 16, I visited Albert in Queensland and when the time came for me to leave, I remember actually feeling happy at the thought of never seeing him again.

Now, I see the words on the pages in front of me and I look closely at the narrow and uneven letters. My 16-year-old thoughts stare back at me, though the pages of an old diary:

Outwardly, he is a man. This is what other people must see. I see a boy in a man's body: a boy who grew old, but never grew up. A Peter Pan. Maybe he is scared to grow up. He thinks he is mature, but he is only being fanciful, just like the animated character. And Peter? Peter was meant to be a good guy, wasn't he?

On the other hand, my father is like Captain Hook. He embraces the ideas of his crew members and calls them his own, taking credit for what isn't his. He pretends to be something he really isn't and thinks everything is his, even though once he acquires something he will neglect it for the rest of his life.

I'll never forget what he said to me once, the lines on his face harsh, his eyes relentless and fiery: 'Your husband will beat and shout at you if you don't cook for him, wash for him and clean up after him.' I looked at him and shook my head. Surely we don't live in that kind of world any more? That is just his belief. I went to bed thinking about what he said to me that night. I didn't want a husband who would beat me or dominate me and tell me how to live and what to live for. I won't fall into that trap; I will not become a victim of that state of mind.

For all the times he pushed me out of his life to make room for another, I will push him further and further out of my life. For putting himself and others before me, I will put him last. For the hurtful things he said to my mother. My mother, who taught us that all adults aren't always right and don't always do the right thing or tell the exact truth, including our father. I thank Mum for letting me decide my own opinion of my father, and for not covering up his mistakes. But most of all, I thank and love her for being there to stand up for me when I didn't know better, especially at such an impressionable age.

I remember one night in particular during my visit. I had packed up my homework, switched off the light and gone to brush my teeth. It was late. I walked past the kitchen where the light was on and looked in. My father was there, eating something of his own concoction.

Between two pieces of last week's stale bread was a thickly sliced piece of mass-produced cold meat oozing with runny tomato sauce. He stood there alone, eating above the bench with no plate under his horrible sandwich. I stood there for a moment, watching him. I watched the way he tore the bread apart with his teeth, saliva dribbling down his face, dripping down onto the crumbs scattered on the bench top. His crumbs would still be on the bench the next day, left behind as always for someone else to clean up. It's understandable, though. He still can't figure out how to use a sponge.

From above the sandwich his eyes looked at me, his lips unable to form words through the mess in his mouth. Would he have said anything, if his mouth were empty? Probably not. Either way, it didn't matter to me. I wasn't interested in what he had to say. It never did make sense to me anyway.

He was feeling sorry for himself again. As neutrally as possible I said that I was going to bed, which I followed up with a hollow 'goodnight'. I had nothing else to offer. I had no sympathy, no love and no respect for him.

That night I knew he would go into the lounge room and fall asleep on his couch in front of the TV, letting it rattle away into the night. As I stood and watched him from the kitchen, I knew that God was providing me with a fine example – an example of what not to become.

Reflecting back on that visit, I realise that I had not made a mistake by going back to Queensland. Rather, I had made a mistake by going there and expecting…I'm not sure exactly what I had expected. Maybe 'expected' isn't the right word. I think I hoped he could have treated me like one of his friends, which had to be better than being treated like a daughter. I wanted the ever-present wall of bitterness between us gone.

If you take someone's love for granted and bash it around, you won't have it for very long, will you? Will you? Does anyone know? I mean, as well as I do? My sustaining thought is that one day I will be completely independent of that man, my father, and possibly every other man in the world, for the rest of my life.

I think of how he humiliated me as a child, people laughing at me, because I was a joke. His joke. The faces of his friends, laughing, haunt me in my worst nightmares and scare me out of my wits. It wasn't fair; they had nothing to laugh about. I learnt to laugh at myself and feel bad afterwards. I know those people today. I consider some friends and they still laugh at what he says, but they don't laugh at me any more. They have found somebody else to feel sorry for, someone they can see losing his daughter. Someone who will find that when he finally grows up he is just a lonely aging man.

6 January 2003

When I showed this part of my diary to my mum, she told me a moving story about Albert and gave me some of his beautiful poems, artwork and photography. She had been keeping them in the attic for more than 20 years. I could not believe he could write or draw like this. She said he wasn't always depressed. I think she was asking me to try to step into Albert's shoes. Now that I think about it, his shoes felt tattered and cold and in need of major repairs, just like his heart and just like his soul.

Fortunately, I have my mum's side. Mum is part of the Wathaurong community in Geelong. I love belonging to this community. My strength comes from my family links and kinship, my extended family, the respect I have for the elders, my friends, my role models, my culture, the land, my spiritual beliefs, and our traditions. My pride comes from my sense of identity, my aspirations, my feelings of respon-

sibility, my sporting achievements and creativity. I am also fiercely proud of our recent history as well as our ancient history.

It must be hard for my sisters, not knowing their background, their real family, their community or their culture.

I have a lot of questions I want to ask these strangers, these two living relations I can call my sisters. Yet I also have a lot of insecurities too. I have had many sleepless nights with these questions racing through my mind. I need to find these girls and put my mind, body and soul at ease. I hope that they will accept me. I know to expect discomfort and shyness, even bitchiness, but I don't expect them to like me straight away. I am feeling so many different emotions that I don't know what I feel. One feeling is resentment, but why should I take it out on strangers when it is my father who I resent? Another is anger, but I already know from my interactions with my father that it would get me nowhere. I'm really jumpy and my heart is always in my throat. Why do I have to find them? Do they know they are of Aboriginal descent? They may not even want to know me. I feel vulnerable and open to pain and rejection, but I'm going to try anyway, regardless of the consequences. After all, I will never know how they feel unless I contact them.

I will write to Christina first.

Adele

Dear Juliet,

I want to tell you about the Dandelion Theory.

The jagged line represents the highs and lows of human emotion. Each peak is a pleasing ascent from a state of discomfort and into a period of contentment. The further that a point sinks below the 'line of middle-most emotion', the higher the degree of 'negative emotion'. Life is a cycle. And our moods continue in a cycle, as we never stop jumping from one state to another. Therefore this jagged line should be circular and look somewhat like an asterisk, to more appropriately represent this giddy cycle of life.

The asterisk shape represents the repetitive and uncertain pattern of human emotion. It's a circular wave of irregular peaks and troughs that form an erratic yet consistent cycle. Each and every tremor in this 'asterisk cycle' has a different intensity, yet the exact same intensity of any one given point is never the same as it was in the cycle preceding it. A path that has been followed once will not be precisely followed again.

The dandelion spore represents the 'asterisk cycle' on a three-dimensional level. The surface of the dandelion spore is a spherical shell covered in peaks and troughs. To follow a path once around this surface represents one complete lap of the 'asterisk cycle'. The dandelion spore symbolises the emotional journey of one person's lifetime and is an approximate physical representation of each and every emotional state felt within the entirety of a lifetime.

And, dust to dust, it will wither beside us.

Albert
9 August 1984

POSITIVE
EMOTION

NEGATIVE
EMOTION

- THE LINE OF
MIDDLEMOST
EMOTION

of the ocean's
decrease,
we moved to
the rhythm
whispered by
the seas

Barely One Word

We walked (our locked hands were love's tender leash)
Where the sand was dismissed of our slow stride,
By soft caress of the ocean's decrease,
We moved to the rhythm whispered by the seas
Over hourglass grains forgotten behind.

We spoke barely one word less or more,
Until asking you for some assistance,
I said: 'Do you think that the waves plea for
A taste of the earth, or is it that the shore
Has a thirst that curves into the distance?'

'Neither...' you replied after staring long
Out at the tide, as you have ever since.
'The waves and the shore crave not to be wronged.
Two lovers like us, they embrace and belong,
And nurse the casualty of our footprints.'

Love YOU

Albert Thompson
August 1984

e memories I have

Without a goodb

There is an em

only you can fi

are mine to keep

went to sleep

I cant

RECENT HISTORY

May 1967: The National Referendum

Australia Day 1971: The Aboriginal Embassy or Tent Embassy was erected in the grounds of Parliament House. This was a powerful symbol of resistance and cultural revival for Aboriginal people who flooded to it to protest poor conditions.

July 1971: The Aboriginal flag was first flown. The flag is symbolic to our people: the black represents the Aboriginal people of the past, present and future; the yellow represents the sun-giver of life; the red represents the earth, red ochre and our spiritual relationship to the land.

1987: Royal Commission into Aboriginal Deaths in Custody

1989: Formation of the Aboriginal and Torres Strait Islander Commission

3 June 1992: The Mabo case was settled. The High Court announced: 'The land in the Murray Islands is not Crown land. The Meriam people are entitled as against the whole world to possession, occupation, use and enjoyment of the Murray Islands.' Terra Nullus was thus replaced with Native Title.

1993: The Native Title Act

1997: Formation of the Council for Aboriginal Reconciliation and the Declaration for Reconciliation

DECLARATION FOR RECONCILIATION

We, the peoples of Australia, of many origins as we are, make a commitment to go on together in a spirit of reconciliation.

We value the unique status of Aboriginal and Torres Strait Islander peoples as the original owners and custodians of lands and waters.

We recognise this land and its waters were settled as colonies without treaty or consent. Re-affirming the human rights of all Australians, we respect and recognise continuing customary laws, beliefs and traditions. Through understanding the spiritual relationship between the land and its first peoples, we share our future and live in harmony.

Our nation must have the courage to own the truth, to heal the wounds of its past so that we can move on together at peace with ourselves.

Reconciliation must live in the hearts and minds of all Australians. Many steps have been taken, many steps remain as we learn our shared histories. As we walk the journey of healing, one part of the nation apologises and expresses its sorrow and sincere regret for the injustices of the past, so the other part accepts the apologies and forgives.

We desire a future where all Australians enjoy their rights, accept their responsibilities, and have the opportunity to achieve their full potential.

And so, we pledge ourselves to stop injustice, overcome disadvantage and respect that Aboriginal and Torres Strait Islander peoples have the right to self-determination within the life of the nation.

Our hope is for a united Australia that respects this land of ours; values the Aboriginal and Torres Strait Islander heritage; and provides justice and equity for all.

COUNCIL FOR ABORIGINAL RECONCILIATION

8 January 2003

Dear Christina,

My name is Adele Thompson. I have recently been told by a great aunt that I have two half-sisters, which is why I am writing to you. I have reason to believe that you are my half-sister. My father, our father, is living in Far North Queensland and is very ill.

I was told by Link Up (the agency I went through to find you) it could take ages to find you and Rachel. But our aunty gave me the dates of birth for each of you, which made it easier for me to track you down. I hope that you are not offended in any way, as I am very anxious and nervous about your reaction.

I will be contacting Rachel's mother to see if she is willing to meet with me. I would like it if you are able to meet with me too. Maybe we could all meet and get to know each other? I hope this can be possible. However, while writing this I have come to a realisation. Did you know you had sisters? If not, then I know that this information may come as a shock to you. But I have already been through it and realise if I don't take this opportunity of contacting you, I would wonder for the rest of my life if we could have become friends, or, even better, feel like sisters.

So please, if you could reply by either phone or letter, I would really appreciate it. I hope that you will consider what I have asked of you. Please, I would like to know who my sister is.

Yours faithfully,
Adele Thompson

10 January 2003

Today I received a letter in the mail from a girl named Adele Thompson. She's claiming to be my sister, well, half-sister! And she also said that we have a younger sister, Rachel. How is this possible?

And on top of it all, she told me my dad's name for the first time. Albert Thompson. A few years ago, I found out about my real mum and that she was Aboriginal, but she died soon after. Her name was Therese Freedman and she was 17 when she had me. I keep the letters from her and the adoption agency and my birth certificate under my bed.

My birth certificate has a line through it where my dad's details are meant to be. Now I know that his name is Albert Thompson and he lives in Northern Queensland.

Adele asked me in the letter to attend a meeting with her, Rachel and Rachel's mother. I thought that I would be too uncomfortable to go to something like that, but then I decided I would go. I need to find out for myself.

My mum cried a lot over this and wouldn't help. Somehow I had driven an even deeper wedge between us by showing her the letter from Adele. She just said that the past is dead and that I should respect that and let it stay that way. Dead. But how can it stay dead when the people are still living?

It is nothing to be ashamed of, or is it? Lately I have been feeling an emptiness within me, like I've had a hole in my life and that something was missing. I've never quite fitted in anywhere. I have always felt that people around me were just pretending I was one of them. Kids at school ask me: 'Why do you look different?' or 'You can't even tell that you're Aboriginal.' I was hurt on Sorry Day when friends said: 'Why do we have to say sorry to you? We didn't do anything wrong.'

I have been to six different schools and now I am at secondary college and it has been hard making new friends. My mum's family doesn't accept me. They ignore me. How does it feel when your own family doesn't want you? I don't talk about it. I just need to feel loved, supported, understood, and to have someone ask: 'How are

you?', 'How are you really?', 'That must be difficult.', 'Is there something I could do to support you?'

They say I will be okay
They say not to cry
So I dry my eye
But the tears won't stop
And all they say is
It will be okay
That's all they say.

What if I had grown up in my real family? Would I have been better off than I am now? Or would it have been worse? How could I
be worse off?

A Silent Wish

A silent wish that you were here
My thoughts of you still bring a tear
Even though I can feel you beside me
The memories I have are mine to keep
Without a goodbye you went to sleep
There is an empty space in my heart only you can fill
I love you now and always will.

Christina

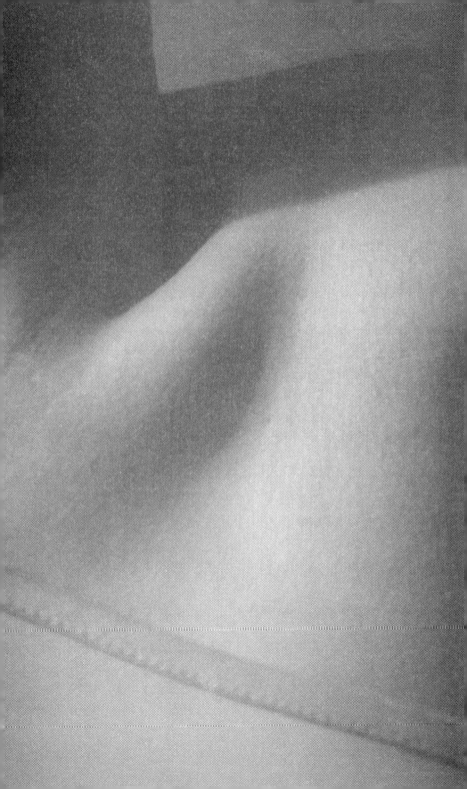

The Adoption Information Service
of the Mission of St James and St John
12 Batman Street
West Melbourne, Vic. 3003

3 January 2000

Dear Mrs Williams,

Under Section 96 of the Adoption Act, 1984, which was
proclaimed in 1985, I have received an inquiry from the
birth mother of your daughter, who was born at the Royal
Women's Hospital on 8.1.1987 and named 'Rosemary' by
her birth mother Therese. Therese wishes to have information on your daughter, and later meet with her, if
she is willing.

The Adoption Act allows such inquiries to be made, provided the inquirer has had a counselling interview with
an approved counsellor. As Therese lives interstate she
has seen an approved counsellor there, and has stressed
that she does not wish to disturb you or your family in
any way. On this point however, she has requested some
information about your daughter. All she asks for is a
reassurance of her wellbeing and happiness. Her other
request is to know what direction her daughter will be
heading in the future, with regard to career and family.

I realise that you may be unprepared for this letter,
and that you may not have told your daughter of her
adoption. For your information, Therese is married but
has no other children.

If you wish to discuss this request with me, please do
not hesitate to contact me. I look forward to hearing
from you, and also from your daughter.

With best wishes to you all,

Mrs Eliza Jane
Social Worker

Therese

23 June 2000

Dear Christina,

You will never know just how it feels to have contact with you after all the years of thinking about you. Wondering if you were alive, and if you were happy. Now I know. In a way my mind is at ease. Still, I know that I have missed seeing you growing up into the lovely looking young woman you are. Your mother's letter describing how you grew up, was beautiful. She obviously loves you very much and you have had a privileged life. Much more so than you would have if you had been with me. She sent me some photos. How lovely they are. I will treasure them. There is so much to tell you that I don't really know where to begin, but I will try my best.

I had a fairly ordinary education, and lived in a bad suburb. I left school at fifteen. When I was sixteen I met your father. It was a strange meeting, we were at a ball, he with Juliet, and me with another boy. We talked and danced all night and exchanged phone numbers. He was a wonderful sportsman. You name it, he did it. But very much a gentle person and a gentleman.

Then I found out I was pregnant. In those days it would have caused a terrible scandal. It must have been just as bad for him as it was for me.

When I told my mother, I was sent to Melbourne. After you were born and I had relinquished you, I returned to Sydney. Albert then told me that he had already left Juliet and that he had met another girl named Nicole and was in love with her. Just like that. It took a long time for me to realise that he meant it, and I gave him a hard time. I hoped, up until the day he married Nicole, that he would change his mind. I vowed that I would never trust a man again. I had not told anyone else about you, so there was no one else to talk to.

You are very like me. I have olive skin and had dark hair, although mine is turning grey, a part of the ageing process I guess.

The last thing I would want to do is intrude into your life when you don't want me to. Always I have always hoped that one day I would find you. I would love to meet you before too much more time goes by. Please write, Christina. I have in past times always thought of you as Rosemary, the birth name I gave you. But as soon as I found out your name, you became Christina to me, a name I like.

Till I hear from you,
I remain your birth mother,

Therese

the charred remains of

goodbye to

leave the

today entering embers of

the fading dust and ashes

ADMITTED

TERMS OF ADMISSION   Adoption

BAPTISED ON   AT

sband's
~~FATHER'S~~ NAME IN FULL

OCCUPATION

MOTHER'S NAME IN FULL

OCCUPATION

ADDRESS OF MOST INTERESTED PERSON

HOW SUPPORTED

CONSENT TO ADOPTION ORDER

MEDICAL EXAMINATION—SENT TO DR.

TESTS

MEDICAL HISTORY—WHOOPING COUGH?

SCARLET FEVER?

ANY OTHER MEDICAL DETAILS

9 September 2000

Dearest Christina,

They are still the two most wonderful words I love to see in print, and they are even lovelier from my own hand. It was great to hear your voice on Thursday evening. Thank you for ringing. I should have written a letter with the parcel, but didn't realise until later that it was school holidays down there too. I am glad you like the nighties. I do hope you had a nice time with your friends on Friday. Bushwalking sounds like a fun way to spend your holidays. Strange what we can do and put up with when we are young and call it fun. I must say I prefer a nice comfortable bed and a nice warm fire.

I am just beginning to write again after having an infected finger. It was just a blister that broke, but didn't heal. My right index finger too, which has inconvenienced me a great deal. I was going to ring you but here I am writing. I am also just getting over a mystery virus and am finding it harder to get out of bed each morning. I listened to a radio programme the other night about adoption. It was very interesting to hear the views of the adopted people and the adoptive parents and, of course, the relinquishing mothers. I was quite surprised by the number of men who phoned in to say they would like help finding adopted children. I would listen to one opinion and think, yes, that's the way I feel, then another would ring and say they did not want to know the mother who gave them away. One girl said she met her mother and instantly disliked her, said she was just a total stranger and they have never met or been in touch again. Anyway, Christina, I know that I don't regret finding you. I know I didn't have anything to do with your upbringing, but I do feel proud of you and you were always with me in thought. At times I feel I will wake up and this will have all been a dream.

Love to you all, Therese

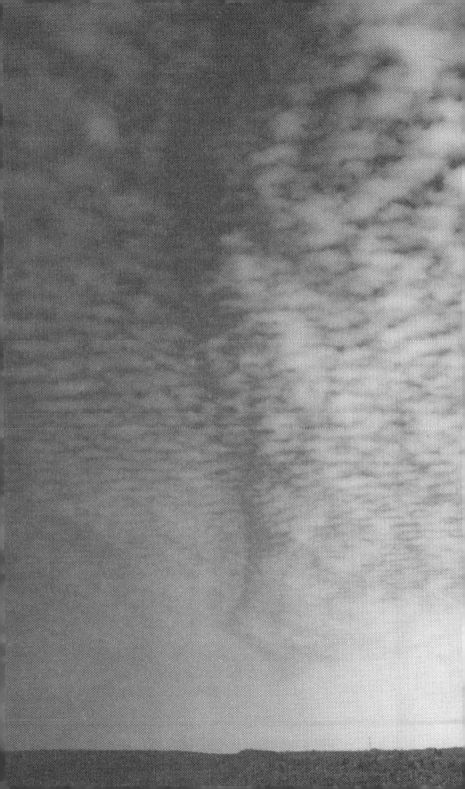

Dear Therese,

The Perfect Match

She is the tender touch wood tinder
That reforms my heart to a furnace.
But our concord my touch would simmer,
For I fear my love for her would only burn us.
If I could collect my confidence,
I would attempt to fuel and fasten
My passion into a blaze of sense,
And wear the tepid title: Guilty of Arson.
To see the charred remains of sadness,
And kiss goodbye the fading embers.
It hurts to leave the dust and ashes,
Fault be mine, I was told not to play with matches.

Albert
4 July 1986

11 January 2003

Dear Diary,

As I dialled the number, I kept thinking, what if they don't want to know me? What if she is not my half-sister? I'm actually scared. My heart is jumping in my throat and I feel really giddy.

I felt the urge to hang up as soon as I heard the phone ringing at the other end of the line, but I had to call and get the conversation over and done with. I wanted to hear Rachel's voice and say to myself that this girl is my flesh and blood. She is my sister.

As the phone rang, I held my breath. My heart was racing and I was quickly running through my mind, thinking of things to say.

'Hello? Nicole speaking.'

Well, here goes… I thought.

'Err, hello? My name is Adele Thompson and I believe that Rachel is Albert Thompson's daughter.'

'Ah…Who are you? How do you know all this?'

'I'm also Albert Thompson's daughter. My Great Aunty Betty Thompson notified me that Albert is in Far North Queensland, dying, and that I have two half-sisters. I went through Link Up and they found the addresses and phone numbers for me. I hope I haven't intruded in any way.'

Long silence.

'You have. It's just that I haven't heard from Albert for almost twelve years.'

'Is it possible that I could meet Rachel? With your supervision, of course?'

'Ah. Can I think about it?'

'Sure, would you like my phone number and postal address?'

'Yes, all right.'

As I hung up the phone, I let out a big sigh of relief. I felt as if I had been holding my breath. But it felt better to get the phone conversation out of the way, even though I did not get to speak to Rachel.

Adele

3: Meeting

11 January 2003

Today, Mum and Dad told me about a phone call they received from a girl named Adele Thompson. Adele is my half-sister and my real dad's name is Albert Thompson.

What was she talking about!? To know that my mother, my closest dearest person my flesh and blood who has brought me into the world and raised me and loved me has deceived me sends my whole perception of my life and my world around me crashing down around my ears. How could she lie? She has been untruthful. I wonder what else she has held back for my own protection. I feel as if I am not myself like I've just met myself for the first time. I feel awkward and clumsy. Who am I? Who do I really belong to? I can't believe this is really happening to me! Things like this do not happen to people like me.

I remember when I was 10 years old, eating my lunch with my mum in a park in Sydney. An old Aboriginal lady started circling us. I thought she wanted food but she stopped about a metre in front of me and just stared. Her old tired eyes wouldn't leave my face and she spoke softly and slowly. 'You an Aboriginal child, eh?' The lady said I should watch out for whitefellas. 'They can't be trusted with nothing.'

Mum told her to go away and called her a crazy old lady. Now I wonder who she was. Perhaps she was related to my real father.

I should have been told. He's my father, whoever he is. I wonder whether he has brown eyes like me? And feet that are wide? Are his genes responsible for me hating cabbage or is it just because it smells bad?

This was the first time I had seen my mum this way. We had always seemed so close, like a secret club nobody else was allowed to enter. I had heard other kids in my class at school complain about their mums. They'd say their mums were 'uncool' and strict, but my mum wasn't like that.

Now I feel something pulling us apart, like all of a sudden there is an invisible rope between us. Mum said I needed to know our family history, but while she was talking about my long-lost father she seemed ashamed. I felt I should be ashamed with her but I couldn't. I loved her too much, but this time we were on a totally different wavelength.

I feel excited and eager to meet these girls. I've been trying to persuade Mum and Dad to have more kids but nothing worked. I am still alone in a great big double-storey house. But now I have this whole other side to our family that is new and unreal. Nothing like this has ever happened to my friends at school. I doubt that they have ever seen an Aboriginal person in their life!

In the end Mum calmed down a bit. Dad was fine too. I guess I was the only one who didn't know the secret.

20 January 2003

On the long drive to see the girls, the car was full of tension. Mum was snappy all the way, until she shut off the engine. I couldn't understand why. I could keep a big secret if I wanted to!

We stopped on the corner of a busy street.

'Mum? I'm not coming in, I've changed my mind.' I blurted it out uncontrollably, my feelings just seemed to be swelling up and vomiting out of my mouth. 'I'm scared, Mum.'

What had happened to me? I didn't mean to be saying all these things out loud. They were true, of course, but not meant for everyone else's ears. Mum smiled. 'Sure, sweetie, that's okay, you stay here. Listen to the radio if you like, but lock the doors.' She rubbed my hand lovingly and her eyes seemed to sparkle as her face creased with a reassuring smile. I wasn't sure if the sparkles were tiny drops of tears forming in the corner of her eyes.

'Wait, no, don't leave. MUUMMM!' I screamed as she slammed the car doors and walked away from me. Mum stopped instantly but she didn't even turn around, she just stuck out her arm for me to hold her hand. I guess she knew me too well.

Rachel

Dear Nicole,

A Branch Of Life

If we are like trees,
And every leaf is a single pleasure
That we received from life,
Then who is he
That stands there naked, leafless,
Like a cold tree in the winter,
With his branches stretching desperately for the
heavens?
And if I were a tree
And my leaves lost their colour,
Would my pleasures fade
And then free-fall, softly, back to earth?
Or would they be comforted by a wind
That would carry them so far beyond life,
And make everything make sense.

Albert Thompson
2 March 1989

who is
he
that
stands
there
naked,
leafless,
like a
cold tree
in the
winter

20 January 2003

Dear Diary,

    I was shaking. I was waiting to meet Rachel, Nicole and Christina at the Courthouse Café in Geelong. I had brought some photos and the family tree. I didn't know if they would bring anything, or what we would talk about. I had planned to talk to them about our father and their Aboriginal heritage, but I still wasn't sure. A part of me was looking forward to meeting them but another part of me was still a bit hesitant. I have photos they sent to me so I would recognise them when we met, but they looked different, not like my sisters at all. I would have thought we would have the same nose or chin or even the same mouth as our father's, but I guess I had hoped for too much.

    I will never forget our first words together.

    'Adele?'

    I look up to see a young girl. I recognise her from the photo. I smile.

    'Christina. How are you?'

    'A little nervous, I guess.'

    'I'm shaking.'

    I see Rachel and Nicole and I wave them over.

    The meeting has begun.

Adele

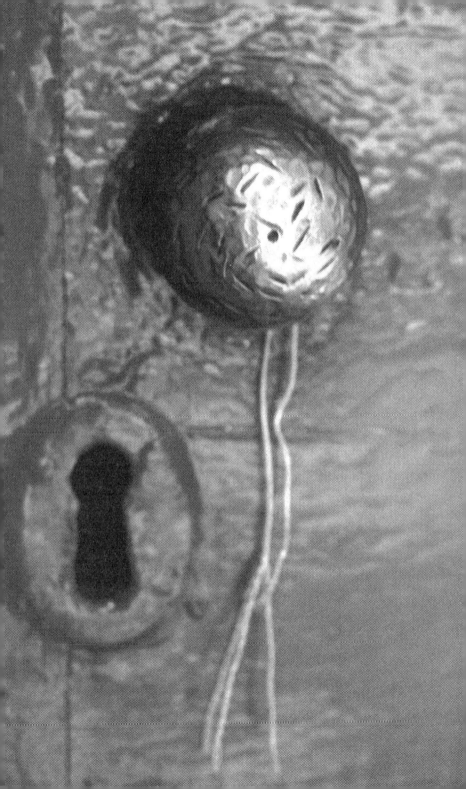

I were a tree

ld my pleasures fade

my leaves lost their col

(fall) softly, back t

20 January 2003

I let go of my mum's hand as we made our way through the tables of people. What was I, two years old? Mum's comforting hand now seemed babyish. I didn't want to seem immature to these older girls.

Trying to think of something to say,
To these strangers called my sisters.
Looking at them, seeing similarities.
Who are they?

The meeting was awkward. I didn't say anything, except mumble a meek 'Hello' to my half-sisters. They were both so much older and prettier than me. I felt shy and I didn't want them to think I was just a kid. After all, I would start Year 9 next week. Adele's finished her schooling and now she wants to do tertiary study. She seemed to have more in common with my mum than me. The two grown-ups did most of the talking. The talk was about my real father, Albert Thompson. It is still an alien name to me. Mum shared heaps of stuff she'd kept. I had no idea about Albert's poetry and artwork. It was strange. Christina and Adele thought the poetry was 'amazing'. I thought it was WEIRD.

Last week I thought Frank was my dad, not Albert Thompson. Listening to a tragic love story involving my mother and another man makes me look at her in a slightly tainted light. Albert Thompson is my real father. Suddenly the most important thing to me is knowing who my real father is.

My sisters were different from what I expected. I thought they would also go to a private school and wear the same cool clothes as me. We were related, weren't we?

In the meeting, things started off slowly and all my enthusiasm seeped away to shyness. I don't think I had had a proper conversation with someone who had completed Year 12 before! Adele seemed very nice. She did most of the talking, unlike Christina who seemed a little sad.

Suddenly I realised this was not a happy meeting. My father, who was still young, was very ill. Adele said my father was also one of the Stolen Generation. In the 1960s, the government took Aboriginal babies from their mothers as they believed the white population could look after the child better.

This part about the Stolen Generation made me feel really sad. I had learnt a little bit about it at school, but it didn't affect me that much. Now I knew someone who had been separated from their mother. I began to imagine what it would have been like. I wonder if Albert ever tried to find his mother again? He must be so mad at the government for ruining his family. The government took children away from their mothers and put them into homes to fend for themselves. They tore families apart. A lot of children were abused and mistreated. Didn't they think about what would happen to these children and their children in the future? Aboriginal people were treated like animals.

On the way home I was really tired. My eyelids were like bricks, but my mind was buzzing. I was wondering how my friends would react at school. Would they care if my runaway dad was Aboriginal? I hoped not. They can be so cruel when they don't like you.

I will always remember one girl who picked on my face. She'd always ask me: 'Why is your nose like that?' or 'What's wrong with your lip?' I didn't think anything was wrong, but she always made me feel self-conscious. If anyone was different from her, you were stupid or weren't allowed into her group. That could ruin your entire school year.

I wasn't sure whether or not to tell my friends. I didn't want them to judge me as someone I wasn't sure I wanted to be. I could feel myself beginning to get angry at my mum. All this time, she had kept quiet. She said that she was only trying to protect me. Protect me from what? I think she's made everything so much worse.

I got out a school essay that I wrote recently. It meant much more to me now. My ancestors have lived in Australia for over 60 000 years!

Rachel

In 1974, at Lake Mungo, geomorphologist Professor Jim Bowler discovered Mungo Man, whose bones have the oldest DNA ever discovered. Mungo Man had been sprinkled ceremonially with red ochre and positioned carefully in a grave with his hands crossed over his pelvis and covered with earth. The skull was anatomically modern. These findings have sparked international scientific debate and shaken the theory of modern man's evolution throughout the world.

This ancient Aborigine is a tool for black and white Australians to learn about the cultural significance of Lake Mungo, a traditional meeting area for Aboriginal tribes including the Mutthi Mutthi, Paakantji and Nyiampa. This is a learning place and a place of respect and spiritual significance.

...owers show their tops in prayer,

...t in tears of dew and nightmar...

...ing for their sun's restorati...

...eak will wake th...

20 January 2003

Dear Diary,

The meeting ran smoothly without a hitch. Although we were all nervous at the start, we began to warm up to each other. Well, that was what I thought. I hope the other girls thought so too.

I basically told the girls about our father, Albert, and that I had been in and out of touch with him. I told them all about me. I also told them about Albert being very ill with diabetes and heart disease and how he also suffers from depression and is a chain smoker. These are common conditions for Aboriginal people and many people smoke because they are depressed. They think smoking is the least of their problems, but it is a major cause of lung disease, cancer, heart disease and stroke.

Obviously Nicole had sheltered Rachel from the truth and Christina seems to know very little about her background. These sisters of mine are different. Christina is from an underprivileged family and Rachel is from a very privileged family, while I am in-between. Rachel showed me her awards and talked about her school achievements. I thought it was sweet.

Christina had also brought her adoption papers and diary and told us about her life. I was intrigued. I forgot to ask her birth mother's surname. She had been through so much and is barely getting through school. I feel really guilty for adding to her problems, but maybe I could help her?

We talked for ages after we got to know each other, and I came up with the idea of putting a scrapbook together for Albert. We ended our meeting with the task of collecting items for the scrapbook and we decided to have a sleep-over at Rachel's house to talk again. I can't wait. They all left with smiles on their faces. I felt relieved and happy.

Adele

'Health does not simply mean the physical wellbeing of the individual but refers to the social, emotional and cultural wellbeing of the whole community. For Aboriginal people, this is seen in terms of the whole life view, incorporating the cyclical concept of life, death and the relationship to the land. Health Care Services should strive to achieve the state where every individual is able to achieve their full potential as a human being of their community.'

VICTORIAN ABORIGINAL COMMUNITY CONTROLLED HEALTH ORGANISATION, 1998

this
path
has
stories
for all
to tell

Dear Nicole,

My August Glow on Evermore

I suspend my steps before the gate,
So to steal a gaze along the straight.
What then from the small shadows could unfold,
Under the dark fall of night's parasol?

The puddles mirror a lid of stars,
Like windows deserving of a glance.
Beauty resides upon their honest aim,
As we may look up whilst head down in shame.

Flowers show their tops in prayers of sadness,
Lost in tears of dew and nightmare tatters,
Praying for their sun's restoration.
Daybreak will wake them at their station.

The pines dance in a dreamy midnight sway,
Their soft trance limbering them for the day.
This path has stories for all to tell,
And, with these few, I bid farewell.

One final march until I find sleep,
And it's there, my Love, that love burns deep.
There you stand, candle in hand by the door,
Shedding my august glow on evermore.

Albert Thompson
29 August 1989

4: Reaction

Dear Nicole,

The Dream-woven Nest

Disarm my dreams of their gardens,
For seeds mature from concepts cradled down
Under ground of rich perception,
And manicured by night's star-buttoned bed-gown.

Arrest the roses of my mind,
The swollen caress of thorns wakens me.
Keep but one to tread the waters
Of a glass cage in the day's vacancy.

Invade the orchards of virtue
And steal the sweetest fruits that midnight jails.
I'll feed the pips to the nightmares
Of the world, if all else fails.

Follow my words, for I am scared
That the gardens of my dreams are lending
A home to a bird that's nesting,
On the fork of my beginning, and my ending.

Albert
2 November 1989

Arrest the
roses of my
mind,
The swollen
caress of
thorns
wakens
me.
Keep but
one to
tread the
waters
Of a glass
cage

28 January 2002

I feel exhausted after the sleep-over but strangely at peace. Adele, Rachel and I talked all night. I laughed until I couldn't breathe. We set up a tent in the middle of Rachel's bedroom and snuggled up in our sleeping bags. It felt comfortable to talk openly about everything.

Rachel told us all about her friends. There are two main groups of kids at her school, the Frenzals who smoke on the oval and the Jocks who are the popular sporty girls with pretty hair and turned-up collars. Rachel doesn't belong to either group and somehow is friends with both. I am an outsider at my school so I understand the pressure to conform, to belong. One day you can belong to a group and the next day you are expelled. Girl-fights can be really nasty. Gossip doesn't mean to hurt people but it hurts if it is about you. It's really hard not to retaliate if people pay you out. But if you just wait, keep your temper and believe the truth, your friends will stick with you. If you have older friends in Year 12, people want to know you. You are popular if you know the right people. It's a status thing.

It seems to be a cultural thing to bag people. At my school, groups of my friends pick on kids from other schools. We also laugh at people with weird clothes: made-up middle-aged women in white and fluoro striped tracksuits with their tracky pants pulled above their waists. People with mullet haircuts. Girls with ugly boyfriends. Sometimes my friends laugh at people who are disabled. One guy had no neck. I just turned away. I didn't want to laugh but I didn't want to lose my friends either. It seems to be human behaviour to criticise anyone different. That's why I don't like to admit that I'm Aboriginal. It's wrong.

I also told Adele and Rachel some ghost stories. One time I was at a camp at Lake Condah. This was a place where Aboriginal people were slaughtered. Every spring there are patches of red flowers over places where people died. Women are not allowed to go over the bridge because of secret men's business but one of the girls did. All the people at the camp were then woken by a sound like a stampede and they quickly ran for the bus. As we drove away from the camp, we could see hundreds of hands beating the bus windows. The bus stopped at a backpackers hostel and at first we were really scared of all these bikies. But you can't judge people by their appearance. The bikies bought us 20 pizzas and taught us how to breakdance. It was really funny. I had just turned 16 and I bought lots of lollies with my first Abstudy payment. I shared them around. The bikies said they expected some Indigenous food, not sherbet, fudge, iced pancakes, Dutch licorice and ollie bollies.

In the morning when Adele was still asleep, Rachel and I covered her face with Frank's shaving cream. We drew a French moustache on her face. Unfortunately it was a permanent marker and she had to work at KFC that day. Adele thought it was a great joke. I guess she has learnt to be really tolerant. Hopefully the marks will come off before her deb ball. I can hardly wait to see my sisters again.

Christina

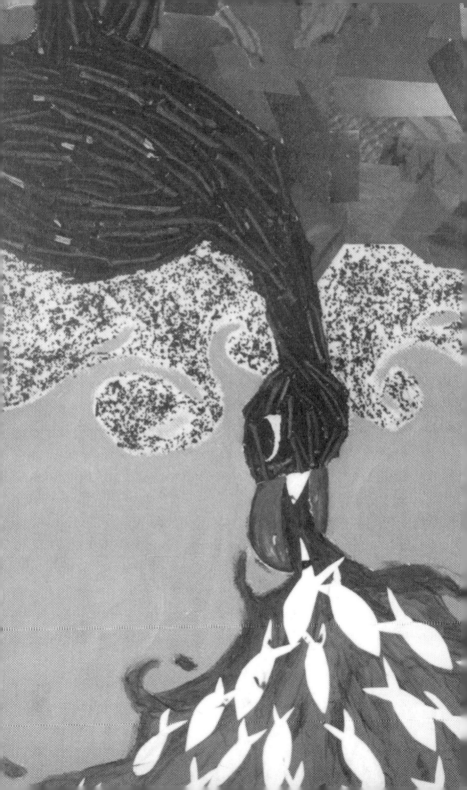

3 February 2003

A few days ago, I had to go to the shops to buy a birthday present for my friend. As we walked near the bus stop, there were all these homeless people sitting around on the concrete. They were asking people for money. Some of them seemed to be Aboriginal. I didn't know there were Aboriginal people in this area. Maybe I just made myself not notice before. I wondered how many other people had a long-lost family like me.

I'm seeing my dad (my step-dad who last week I thought was my real dad) in a new way. I think my relationship will change with him. At the moment I feel like he's just a man living in my house. Like a relative you haven't seen before. There have been heaps of awkward silences, which would usually be filled with chatter. I think he feels I might not accept him now that I've found out about my real dad. My step-dad is not Aboriginal, but he has always been concerned about Aboriginal issues.

But I'm not sure if I really feel my real dad is my dad! How can Albert expect me to feel close to him instantly when I've never met him. I'm not sure if I want to meet him, considering he left my mum because he couldn't cope when I was only a baby.

I'm so confused. I don't know what to think! Everything around me is changing, but I'm staying the same. It's like everyone has read this really great book and knows all the details and I'm the only person who doesn't know the story.

It is a coincidence that we are studying Aboriginal culture at school. A woman from the local Koori community came to our school. While she was talking to everyone about her culture, I felt proud, I felt as though I belonged to an exclusive club. By the end of our lesson, I was about to explode because I wanted to tell everyone about my new family and heritage. I wanted everyone to know I was like her. But I didn't say anything.

I guess I was surprised by the class reaction to her. Most of my class only see Aboriginal people on the news after they've been sniffing petrol all day – the bad stuff only. But yesterday everyone was taken aback by a really beautiful young woman, who had the confidence to share her culture with a white community who had been abusing her family for more than 200 years.

I don't think my friends had ever considered the black Indigenous people of Australia to be beautiful before. I have heard people praise black Americans in music video clips, saying they wished they were like them, but yesterday was the first time I heard anyone praise black Indigenous people.

Later I had the chance to spill my secret. I was invited over to my best friend's house for a sleep-over. We played this game where you all go around in a circle and tell a secret you've never told anyone before. I asked the girls not to tell anyone because I don't think I could handle the teasing and taunts I've seen some kids get because of their culture. So now everything is fine! At least for now, I hope. Things have been very different at home.

Rachel

Dear Producer,

I am writing to you regarding the program screened on Channel 9's 'A Current Affair' debating the fairness of the University of Newcastle Medical School's entrance criteria for Aboriginal students.

Since when has the formal education process ever been fair for Aboriginal students? Aboriginal and Torres Strait Islander peoples are the poorest, unhealthiest, least employed, worst housed and most imprisoned Australians.

The 2003 Report on Government Services stated: 'For all schools apparent retention rates from Year 10 to Year 12 for Indigenous students in 2001 ranged from 59.1% in Queensland to 26.9% in W.A. About 10-20% of Indigenous students leave school before Year 10 (although school is compulsory at this stage). Nationally, Indigenous retention from Year 10 to Year 12 for all schools in 2001 was 31.8 percentage points lower than for all students.'

The report also documented literacy and numeracy levels of a significant percentage of Indigenous students in primary school as being well below the benchmark.

Education does not simply supply knowledge. Its outcomes provide opportunity, hope and, most importantly, choice. The University of Newcastle is to be applauded for its entrance policy that provides a window of opportunity for young Aboriginal people.

The enlightened policy-makers at this institution and similar bodies such as Deakin University have realised that only by providing educational opportunities to Aboriginal people will true reconciliation take place.

This is where Aboriginal students, through the educative process, can act as role models for their people, be involved in the political decision-making process and be provided with that freedom of opportunity.

Frank Roberts

'Indigenous children have been forcibly removed from their families and communities since the first days of European settlement. In that time, not one Indigenous family has escaped the effects. Most families have been affected in one or more generations by the removal of one or more children. Nationally, the inquiry concludes that between one in three and one in ten Indigenous children were forcibly removed from families and communities between 1910 and 1970.'

'BRINGING THEM HOME'
NATIONAL INQUIRY 1995

'Australia is a country where the right to live free from unfair treatment is protected by law. This is called the right to equal opportunity and this right is protected by the Racial Discrimination Act, the Sex Discrimination Act and the Disability Discrimination Act 1992. Discrimination means treating a person who has a certain personal characteristic less favourably than a person who does not have that characteristic. It is against the law to discriminate on the basis of race, religion, sex, age, disability, physical features, political beliefs or pregnancy.'

EQUAL OPPORTUNITY
COMMISSION

The good son
He does as he's asked
But only when it suits him
Yet you don't see it
You treat me like dirt
Love me only when it suits you
You don't see it
You only see the bad son…me.

What do I want?
How can I tell you
When all you do is criticise
Find the faults in my aspirations
Make me feel stupid and naïve
Show me I'm a failure
Even in my dreams
I told you what I wanted
Wrote it down and showed you
You spat it back in my face
I trusted you

Albert Thompson
1977

3 February 2003

Dear Rachel,

I know you're probably cross with me.

I've been thinking over and over about your words of last night. 'Mum, why didn't you tell me?' Over and over again. We always sensed that you knew there was a secret. We know you. We know how sometimes you were so sad, especially at certain times of the year. Somehow families just know about secrets. They just don't really know what they are. We always felt you were missing something, or maybe even someone.

Well, it was the shame, the shame of not enough food, not enough money and not enough room. It was better to go away, to put it behind me. Your step-dad always knew the truth. He is the kindest, most generous man. He doesn't want to see me hurting. But the hurt has never gone away.

So now it's time to hear about your real dad. He was so handsome and fun. You look like him and I can also see his charm in your personality. He loved you, but he also loved life in a way that meant he was out late and meeting other people. They used to know him at all the clubs. Often he didn't come home. I always knew he was staying with one of his many friends. But my family was really cross with him, at the way he was always away. They were really protective of me. They pushed him away and out of our family. I know how he felt because we met once and talked about how he missed you. He was scared to make contact, never sure of how we would feel about him. But I've never forgotten him.

I hope you will forgive me for keeping this secret. I only wanted to protect you from being hurt by the truth.

With love,
Your mum,
Nicole

Confirmed at .....

By .....

H. H.

Occupation		Whe Emplo
Address		
UNKNOWN		

Dr.'s Repo .....

for Exam .....

4 February 2003

Dear Christina,

It sounds as though you are finding it hard to stay at school.

Achieving my VCE was hard. I was sick a lot and I didn't know what was wrong with me. I struggled with chronic fatigue. If I hadn't had the support of the teachers and my mum, I would have been 'just another statistic' to put in the books. Not many young Aboriginal people get through Year 12. But I did and I'm proud of myself. So is my mum and her family.

Now I'm eighteen and I'm going to the Gordon TAFE to build up to university studies. I didn't want to push myself after completing my VCE. I don't think I would be able to handle the workload at uni.

I'm glad I got through school. At one stage I wanted to drop out because of the racism and taunting. I used to cry every night and take my anger and pain out on Mum. But I eventually learned to ignore it, and I stayed away from students who made racist jokes and remarks.

I got sick of my history teacher asking if a certain historical event or fact was correct. She was always singling me out in class. She should have known if the event or fact was correct. She was a teacher, after all. One day after class I told her not to ask me because I'm still learning about my culture. I don't have all the answers.

One of my friends said that Kooris got too much money from the government and wasted it on alcohol and cigarettes. I was so angry, but instead of taking it out on her, I wrote an essay for Year 11 English to explain to her and the rest of the English class that not all Aboriginals waste their money – many do spend the money on school fees and books. I still have that essay. But I am no longer friends with that girl.

The government is not helping by cutting funding to Aboriginal affairs. I went to a protest in Canberra in Year 10. My brother and I linked hands with everyone around Parliament House and then later marched from the bottom of the hill to the front of Parliament.

I worry about my brother sometimes. He used to be a really chubby boy but within the last two years he started shedding weight. He's anorexic and it scares me. I told Mum but she says not to interfere. He has been smoking dope since Grade 6 and the first time he got really drunk was at my friend's 19th birthday party, yelling out, 'I love you, Adele, I'm sorry!' Although he is always getting into trouble, I love my brother.

Christina, you said that you have problems with learning. My brother had problems with this too and I thought it might help you to read about his experience while he was at school. He wrote this:

From Grade 5 to Year 11 was the hardest time for me, growing up. I was meant to take tablets to help me with learning. They changed my mood, changed my personality and I wasn't as talkative with my friends. But I did find that I was able to concentrate for longer periods of time and homework plans were all organised.

Over my whole schooling life, I was given heaps of help from teachers and tutors. In Year 10, I had a tutor for English in all my English classes. I didn't like this because she was in the classroom with me and all the other students knew she was only there to help me, nobody else. That made me feel really stupid.

In Year 10 at school, one day we had a sports day. It was lunchtime and I knew that I had to take my tablets. But how? All my friends were around and would see. So I decided not to take them. One of my friends had no food for lunch, so he started going though our bags to see if we had any food. He found my tablets. I pretended that I didn't see him. My friends went all quiet. I didn't like the way they reacted. They pretended that they didn't know anything. But I knew. I was scared of what my friends were thinking.

I guess I started taking drugs because I didn't have any confidence. At one point I was using every drug I could get and it became so bad that my mum and friends told me I was heading for my death bed. I was in and out of hospitals for trying to kill myself and overdose.

But after a while, you get sick and tired of your life revolving around drugs. One day, I woke up questioning what sort of life this was, and I felt that I deserved better. So did my family and friends. I didn't realise that heroin had such a tight hold of me. I used heroin because I thought it took all my pain away and made me feel better. It did make me feel good. But I had to go out and steal things to support my own habit. I did so many things wrong while I was on the gear and now I look back and think about everything I did and I don't believe it.

Now I have left school and have a job with Wathaurong Glass, which is owned and operated by the local Aboriginal community. Without my friends and my community I don't know where I would have ended up.

I couldn't say that I am privileged, but I guess that the opportunities were there, so I took them. One opportunity was a scholarship from the Alfred Bequest Foundation which was a two-year scholarship of $750 per year. That scholarship encouraged me to finish my VCE.

I had an average report of As, Bs, Cs and Ds. It contained mainly Cs, but it was all right. Some of my classmates didn't seem to think so. The school published my achievement in the school newsletter without asking me for permission and I felt like a trophy they wanted to show off. I didn't want to face my classmates because I knew what their reaction would be: 'Oh, you just got that scholarship handed to you because you're Aboriginal' or 'Why did you get that scholarship when your grades aren't good enough?' I hated it.

I was determined to make a difference with my life. I didn't want to end up on unemployment benefits. I wanted something more. I wanted to go on to tertiary studies and become a social worker to help my Aboriginal people and get them out of the 'cycle'. When opportunities were laid out in front of me, I wasn't going to let them pass me by. I took them. If the other students could not see my goals then they were obviously ignorant.

Ignorance

They stand with their backs turned toward you,
They refuse to listen to your views.
They are ignorant – but what more can you do?
They have this theory – ignorance is bliss.
I believe that ignorance is blind.

Another opportunity was ATAS, which is the Aboriginal Tutorial Assistance Scheme. That basically allowed me to have a tutor to help me with my studies. Having a tutor helped me a great deal. Without ATAS, I don't think I would have finished my schooling. But sometimes ATAS cannot provide the right tutors for the subjects we do. Sometimes they can't provide tutors at all.

Then there was the Koori educator who came to the school to help us with any problems that arose, such as racism or education inequities. Many students also have problems with their health – STDs, pregnancy, depression, smoking, drugs, alcohol, asthma. They don't like going to Aboriginal services because they are concerned about confidentiality and they don't trust mainstream health services and GPs. We used to have a Koori youth health worker to link us in with services, but his position was defunded. Because of this lack of support, a lot of Koori students struggle through school – like my brother.

Adele

What do I want?

How can I tell you

When all you do is criticise.

Find the faults in my aspirati

MANDATORY SENTENCING

Mandatory sentencing is a law that means you have to go to jail after you have committed three offences. Even if you are a child and have committed three small offences (such as stealing a cookie tin), you would immediately be sentenced to jail. Mandatory sentencing applies in the Northern Territory and Western Australia.

Mandatory sentencing mostly affects Indigenous children. On average, the ratio of Indigenous children to non-Indigenous children going to jail (because of mandatory sentencing) is nine to one. This means that every time a non-Indigenous child gets sentenced to jail, on average, nine Indigenous children do as well.

Considering only 20% of Northern Territory people are Indigenous Autralians, this figure is extremely large.

Mandatory sentencing went very wrong when a 15-year-old boy had committed two criminal offences and then stole a pencil and other products worth under $50. He got sentenced to jail. He then committed suicide while in jail.

Most Australians want mandatory sentencing to stop, and so do I. Why can't people ask why Indigenous children are offending? Why? Why?

Adele Thompson, Year 12

ATTITUDES TOWARDS THE FUNDING OF INDIGENOUS AFFAIRS

Misconceptions about Indigenous Australians have gone unanswered for many years. People think that there is too much 'special treatment' and 'money thrown at Indigenous affairs'. I would like to examine the reasons for these attitudes in detail and attempt to show that these common assertions are false.

The first of these assertions is 'there's too much money thrown at Indigenous affairs'. In fact, many Indigenous programs are put in place to compensate for the lack of accessibility to programs such as Austudy which are provided to the rest of the community. The cost of programs such as Abstudy are relatively inexpensive but they cause a great deal of resentment. One author said: 'Special Aboriginal programs are lightning rods for expressions of white resentments.'

Another regularly voiced misconception is that 'Aboriginal people get special treatment from governments'. In reality, most groups with defined special needs within Australian society are able to get special consideration. It is indisputable that the needs of Indigenous people are great when we consider certain statistics. People of Aboriginal descent are likely to die on average 15 to 20 years earlier than other Australians, and suffer more infectious and chronic diseases such as diabetes, ear disease, trachoma and renal failure than non-Aboriginal people.

Without going into any historical justification for compensation, Indigenous people have a strong and ongoing claim for support in relation to special needs. At the time of the introduction of the education assistance scheme, there were only five or six Indigenous Australians enrolled in universities. Now there are over 8000. Thus, the only way forward is to continue to assist all groups of Australians who are in need. If all disadvantaged groups are given government assistance, then Indigenous people may no longer bear the brunt of social criticism from those who feel unfairly treated.

Adele Thompson, Year 12

ABORIGINAL HEALTH
George Megalogenis

Many Aborigines begin their lives in a subclass and many stay there. The most compelling measure of how a nation treats its citizens is the data of life and death. Unfortunately, the life expectancy of Indigenous people has fallen since 1995 in the three states for which comparable official figures are available – for men in Western Australia and for women in South Australia and Northern Territory.

More tellingly, Aborigines appear to be going backwards as the rest of us can look forward to surviving for longer than before. Life expectancy for non-Aboriginal men is to their mid 70s, and for non-Aboriginal women, to their early 80s. The life expectancy gap between Aboriginal men and non-Aboriginal men generally ranges from 14.3 years in the Northern Territory to 22 years in South Australia. For women, the gap runs from 13.6 years in the Northern Territory to 19.6 years in South Australia.

No other developed nation boasts such a split personality: the virtual guarantee of a healthier, more affluent life for people of all skin tones and tongues, but a quicker death for the blacks who were here all along. Australia's Indigenous people also suffer significantly higher death rates than Native Americans in the US and Maoris in New Zealand.

Aborigines make up barely 400 000 out of a total population of 19.1 million. The Prime Minister said earlier this month that $2.3 billion was being spent every year on 'Indigenous-specific programs'. The mischievous in our community would do the maths and claim that Aborigines are getting a pretty good deal from the taxpayer, so their ongoing problems must be of their own making.

But some of that money is used for basics, such as getting clean water to remote communities. Also, the taxpayer cake is cut more equally than many realise. Indigenous people get roughly the same amount of funding per head for their health needs as the rest of us. Given their shorter life expectancies, it stands to reason that they need substantially more help than the typical well-fed, well-paid Australian.

It could be the cliché of our centenary that more needs to be done for the nation's original inhabitants. Not only more money but more than just money.

This is not to suggest that no progress has occurred. The last one-third of Australia's first century has seen Aborigines recognised in the Constitution; land rights; the Mabo Native Title judgment (which the main political parties accept); and the kudos of having hundreds of thousands of ordinary folk marching in the name of reconciliation.

However, the hard numbers warn that Indigenous people will remain an underclass unless attitudes shift further.

Just ask Howard. He supports this supposedly radical view. This is what he said in his final speech of the year: 'I regard Australia's social cohesion, born out of a distinctive form of egalitarianism, as the crowning achievement of the Australian experience during the (past) 100 years. Yet we can never feel satisfied, nor can we feel complete, until that cohesion is expended throughout all sections of the community and specifically until Indigenous Australians enjoy the same opportunity and the same plentiful lives as any other Australian.'

Perhaps he could start by saying sorry for what this generation does share responsibility for: we are the only developed nation in the world to allow a section of the population to face a diminished life expectancy.

In 1770, Captain Cook wrote of Australia's Indigenous peoples that, 'They may appear to some to be the most wretched People upon the Earth; but in reality they are far more happier than we Europeans... They live in a tranquility which is not disturbed by the Inequality of Condition.

The Earth and Sea of their
own accord furnishes them
with all things necessary
for Life.'

All this soon changed, of
course. Aborigines and
Torres Strait Islanders
were not included in the
universal suffrage granted
to Australian men and women
in the Commonwealth Act of
1902. In 1949 the
Commonwealth Electoral Act
gave Aborigines a
Commonwealth vote if they
were enrolled in their state
and/or had completed mili-
tary service. In 1962 this
was amended to include all
Indigenous peoples, but
perversely it was illegal to
encourage them to enrol, a
bizarre state of affairs
which persisted until 1984
when compulsory enrolment
and voting was introduced.
In the 1967 referendum, 90
per cent of white
Australians voted for
Aborigines to be included in
the census as citizens
rather than flora and fauna.
Other Indigenous concerns
remain unaddressed.

THE WEEKEND AUSTRALIAN

Dear Therese,

Wish upon a star

Every day I'd wish upon a star
Wishing you weren't far
Now my wish is different
Now my wish comes true
All I ever wish for
Is never to forget you

Broken Heart

A million words won't bring you back
I know because I have tried
Never will a million tears
I know because I've cried
You've left behind some broken hearts
But I never wanted memories
I only wanted you

Christina

experience you a... not

...saha not perfect, no

...feelings hidden away

...wote starts to ex...

like dogs on st...

the words get

the book gets

in Register — — —	
ription—	
ne and surname — — —	
nk or profession — — —	
and age — ... —	
en and where died — —	
ual Residence — — —	
ere born, and how long in the stralasian Colonies or States, icating which — — —	
me and surname of father —	
nk or profession — — —	
me and maiden surname of mother — — —	
eceased was married—	
here — — — — —	
what age — — — —	
whom — — — —	
njugal condition of deceased at time of death — — —	
sue in order of birth, their names d ages — — — —	
me, description and residence of formant — — —	
use of death — — —	
uration of last illness — —	
edical attendant by whom certified	
hen buried or cremated —	
here buried or cremated —	
ndertaker or Superintendent by whom certified — — -	
ame and religion of Minister .	
ames of witnesses — — .	
gnature of Registrar General, date.	25th Oc

CALL FOR REVIEW OF
ABORIGINAL FUNDING

A Federal Government inquiry has proposed a revolutionary way to fund Aboriginal communities, because it says the system does not do enough about their long-term disadvantage. The draft report advocates an enhanced role for ATSIC, whose regional councils could link state-level decision making with local community control over service delivery matters.

The Commission is highly critical of the way that specific-purpose funds from the Commonwealth, including health funding, are delivered to Indigenous communities.

The report said that spending should 'reflect the long-term nature of Indigenous disadvantage and include a commitment to sustained action and funding'.

hate is destroyed

My baby, Adele,

Hiding Away

Pain caused by others
Pain upon ourselves
Forced into our lives
Driven into our mind

The heart gets colder
The words get harsher
Life drags on slowly
Hate starts to explode

Feelings hidden away
From watchful eyes
Love not experienced
Unknown and unwanted

Somebody listens
Then they understand
Hate is destroyed
Love is finally found

Albert Thompson
1 February 1985

6 February 2003

Dear Adele,

Thanks for your letter about your experiences of school and your brother. I was nearly expelled last year – for wagging for a few days after I had been drunk at a party. There is another reason why I am finding it hard to stay at school. I have never told anyone about this. But I feel that I can trust you.

It will never happen to me. That's what I thought back then. Well, I suppose I didn't really think about it. It seemed like such an impossible event that I didn't think and wound up where I did.

For a whole week, I just walked around in a daze, I couldn't think about anything except 'baby'. Why? I was drunk, I know it's not really an acceptable excuse, but it's the way it was. The father? He's older, in his 20s. I did tell him I was pregnant and he told me it was my problem.

I was terrified. Suddenly, I had a whole new person to think about. How would this person affect my life? The only thing I knew for certain was that it was up to me. I was only 15, still at school, and having worked with kids I knew what a huge responsibility they are.

I knew I could never ever kill a child. Once I knew that, I started thinking about the little baby growing inside me, and that's when I knew I couldn't part with him. Him? Yeah, I just had this feeling it was a boy, don't know why. But then came the severe cramps and the bleeding.

I just stopped. Everything around me stopped. I was nowhere and couldn't get anywhere. I never told Mum. I mean, I was going to, but then it was too late and I just didn't have the energy to explain.

For a long time, I felt nothing. Not just about the baby, but about everything. I felt no pain, no grief, no joy, and not even hunger. I stopped eating, sleeping and working. My school work went downhill very quickly and people started to notice. I never thought it would happen to me. My mistake was that I didn't think.

I felt suicidal after the miscarriage. But nothing is ever bad enough for suicide. I wouldn't ever do it. I've also given up the alcohol and drugs. I just needed someone who would listen to how I felt. I guess that is how Albert felt when he wrote those poems.

Now I feel as though I know some of the fear that my real mum, Therese Freedman, experienced when she had me. I have also discovered a secret: my real mum was related to your mum, Juliet. This means we are sisters and cousins. Knowing I belong to your family makes all the difference. I feel as though I have come a long way since the next diary entry I am sending you.

Christina

8 April 2002

Do you ever think about the stars? How they shine away up there in the sky, surrounded by a blanket of darkness? They provide light on the darkest of nights, penetrating the blackness.

I wish upon a star. Wish. Wish for what? If I had three wishes, what would they be? Life, liberty and the pursuit of happiness. What a joke. Americans and their ignorant pursuit of happiness. Do they really believe there is true happiness? Look at the girl who has everything, money, fancy clothes, a loving family and a nice home. Look at the girl whose parents divorced when she was a mere child, when she didn't yet understand life, whose baby died, who trusts no one, who watches other people. Watches other people and their lives. Wishes she had a friend or two, a real friend or two. Wishes she had something to look forward to, wishes she had even a glimmer or hope. Hope is a word people use to describe the future. But she wishes for something more than that.

Does she have a future? She can't see any hope for her, she can't even see a future. How can someone who has nothing see anything for her? Why does she not tell someone of her nothingness in life? She has; she told people who only betrayed her and left her alone, more alone than she ever has been before.

She imagines she is in a river. A river that was once calm. Then little ripples start to lap onto the shores. Little boats start to pass by her; she waves to them but they don't wave back. She is starting to swallow water. She calls out to the passing boats, help me, help me please, I think I'm drowning. But still they ignore her. Now boats are speeding past her, spraying water all over her. She is swallowing even more water. She can't breathe. She is sinking. Sinking into the depths of the murky water, watching her life fly by above her with every boat that passes overhead. She is trying to swim to the top, but she can't move her arms. There is nothing to do. Her lungs are bursting. Her heart is hurting. She remembers her wish.

She sits alone, looking at the stars, hoping that this sinking feeling will leave her. She reaches out for the stars, they are too far, they are too bright. The light blinds her. Nothing is clear, it is all blurred,

122

she can't see the edges, the picture is no longer clear. Purple, red, yellow, blue. They start from everywhere and end nowhere. They melt together. A murky brown mess surrounds her, she reaches for the weeds, trying to stop herself from sinking further, if only she could pull herself up, if only a passing boat would stop and rescue her. She remembers something. SOS. She tries to send out an SOS, but no one can see, no one wants to see it, they all have somewhere else to go, things to do, they are too busy to bother with her. They are going to let her drown. She wishes.

She has but one wish left, one glimmer of hope. She sinks further, the water is dark and cold here, she can no longer see the surface, she has come too far down. She knows that it is time. Time to realise her wish, her one glimmer of hope.

She can see now, the stars are lighting the dark waters. Little rays of lightness shoot through the water, leaving trails of bubbles behind them. Wish upon a shooting star.

She screams out her silent wish. The emptiness echoes around her with such deafening force she screams again, again, again, again. She wishes, she wishes. Her lungs fill with water, her head is heavy, her heart is tearing her apart. But still she screams her silent wish.

She loses consciousness, her mind fills with blackness, while she blends in with the water. The stars stop shooting. Her lungs stop breathing, her brain stops thinking, her voice stops screaming, her heart stops beating.

Who said wishes don't come true?

Christina

Cemetery

Which one to choose,
they're all the same?
What makes them different?
Old, new, they're all dead souls.

The pines do little to protect the
weathered graves. Stone crumbles from
the corners, suggesting the unveiling
of what's below.

Gargoyles grin over the dead,
a symbol of who they were.
The metal fences lean out of line and
ivy tangles itself wherever it wants.

The heedless growth smells fresh.
The bull ants tunnel.
An old pipe sticks oddly out of the earth.
The steep slope barely contains death.

Poor Elizabeth Holmes deceased 1941.
On her plot stands a monstrous pine.
Is she still below?
I can't decipher the headstone. I don't want to.

Jars of dirty water sit groggily on the
top of the graves. The 'forgotten' end of the
cemetery is where graves lie unvisited,
not maintained, holding nobodies.

Broken tombstones, stubborn roses,
piles of dirt, trees mark the plot.
I don't want to sleep here.

Albert Thompson

suggesting
the
unveiling
of
what's
below

5: The Secret

Dear Therese,

Waiting for the chance to be free

I sit there in the darkness
Willing for your presence close by.
The time is right and I am keen
To leave the life I lead now,
A life that I cannot stand,
That I cannot wait to leave.

I feel the wings embrace me
And see the shadow on the floor.
I always knew you were there
Waiting for me, just watching
For the perfect time to take me.
You knew it would come soon.

Your touch is surprisingly warm,
An unexpected but pleasurable feel
After the cold inside me for so long.
I thought you would be cold,
And even though your touch is warm,
I shiver as you embrace me.

I hear you whisper in my ear
A soft nothingness that's soothing.
Your voice surprises me too,
For it's soft, clear and quiet.
So many unexpected surprises
As I sit there still waiting.

Suddenly your grip becomes tighter
And I feel you draining my life,
Yet I still sit here as alive as before
And you slowly loosen your grip.
Confusing, upset now, I'm afraid,
I'm ready to go, I don't want to stay.

A whisper in my ear again,
Only this time it's clear,
'It's not your time yet,
Remember it can never be that bad.'

Albert Thompson
6 December 1987

'Please would you allow me
to have my two daughters
with me here. Another one
of them died and I have not
seen her before she died
and I should like the other
two, to be with me and comfort me.

'Please do not disappoint
me for my heart is break-
ing to have them with me.
Please to send them up here
as I cannot leave this station. Please to ask Mr
Stahle to let them come.'

MARGARET HARRISON
ABORIGINAL RESIDENT OF
EBENEZER STATION IN 1884
(from 'My Heart is
Breaking', A Joint Guide to
Records about Aboriginal
People in the Public Record
Office of Victoria)

4 February 2003

Dear Adele,

By now you may have caught up with your sisters, and I thought it might help to provide them with the small amount we know about our family's history.

In the 1950s and 1960s, we lived near the Framlingham settlement. One Tree Hill is 12 miles from Warrnambool. All my family lived there but they are all dead now.

I constantly faced many difficulties when I was younger – housing, health, education and fear of being taken away.

I only started talking of the Stolen Generation 14 years ago. It was very upsetting. I have memories of police asking the teacher for kids and taking them out of school – kids were screaming and crying. My family, the other kids and myself were so scared. If a strange car came down the road, we would run down to the river and hide in fear of being taken. Albert is 10 years younger than me and I used to grab his hand and cling to it until they were gone.

The house had three bedrooms and a kitchen and lounge room in one. There was no running water, no bathroom. We only had a stove for warmth, and to wash ourselves we had to use a tub or a dish. Later on, a laundry was added, where we used to wash by hand. Tank water was added on, too.

My youth was different from today's young people's. At school, stuff was written on the board. There were 40 Aboriginal kids in one school with one white teacher. It was the only Aboriginal school in school sports history to win the shield five years in a row.

Our parents and grandparents were strict. We weren't allowed to get away with anything. It was a loving family, though. They taught us kids right from wrong. Our family was careful because kids were being taken and they didn't want harm brought to us. So we weren't allowed to hang around the streets like today. There were a lot of things we weren't allowed to do. I wasn't allowed to go anywhere much and I wasn't allowed to speak language around white people or we'd get taken.

We kept ourselves busy. We spent a lot of time at the river. We walked down there and walked across the stones. We'd go fishing and catch eels and fish. We'd chop wood or play games with the other kids.

When the Welfare came, we had to keep the place clean and spotless with food in the cupboards or we'd get taken away. The food was mainly bread and fat. I can't eat fat today.

Our education was poor then. We had no high-school education because we were Aboriginal. I left school at 14 when I ran away after Albert was taken away. Later, I went through many jobs and became a musician and an artist. I painted Koori art, landscape and seascape. I wrote songs from around home, about my culture and 'Koori English'. I even have a song on a CD that has our language – to keep it alive for future generations.

I finished my teaching degree in 1988 and went into teaching in 1989 at the uni, but I will never forget my childhood.

I will never forget how we were treated in those days. Because we were black, it meant we were nothing. There was a lot of racism back then, and even today, the depth of racism in Australia is apalling. Albert was very deeply affected by being taken away from his family when he was four years old. He does not remember his family but he has never forgotten the day he was taken away. I have always kept this story that he wrote at school.

Great Aunty Betty

All I Wanted To Do Was Play…

All I wanted to do was play. I wanted to swim in the creek and weave through the trees. I wanted to chase the birds and scare them enough so I could hear the sounds of wings flapping and watch their feathers fall around me. I wanted to run free in the bush and collect the different coloured bark. I wanted to lift up rocks and branches to see if I could find another but smaller world of insects. I wanted to watch them go about their day, collecting food and surviving. Just like we were…surviving. I remember following my father as he set off to hunt for food. I remember watching our whole community working together to survive. But what I remember most was not the surviving…but the things we did in between. We had fun. We would dance and sing around the fire…dress up in our paints and be one with the earth. God's great earth, which we praised for giving us everything we needed to live and love.

These memories, however, only go so far. For they are all pushed to the deepest corner of my mind when the darkest memory of my life begins to resurface. The memory of being torn and ripped away from my own family, from everything that I knew and loved, from everything that I needed to survive. I can never forget that day when the 'whites' came and put me in the back of a vehicle with other Aboriginal children. I remember the distressing cries of my mother as she gave me one last touch, a squeeze of my hand before being pulled away from her. I remember the countenance of my father as he watched me disappear into the distant sun – his lowered head and shrunken shoulders, the physical signs of powerlessness. I remember the cold feeling of sitting down on the metal surface of the vehicle and the tears that rolled down my face as we were taken away. I remember that first night I spent in a draughty orphanage where I cried myself to sleep, wishing that I could be with my family and with my land…the land that I knew so well. I remember the rest of the nights where I did the same thing every night...I yearned and cried for what I knew. I remember the day that I lost all hope of surviving...the day I realised that I would never see my home and family again. That was the day my soul died. But the most distinct memory of this horrific day was that despite everything that had happened within that one day, all I wanted to do was play...

Albert Thompson

One Tree Hill

Outside our kitchen window towers
what I call One Tree Hill.
Beaten by time and sky, an ashen
gum stands alone on the tip of
the western hill. An almost perfect
dome shape, it is strangled by the
tracks of sheep hoofs carved deeply.
The tree grabs the gaze of all.
Not moving, not growing.
Dad claims the hill was 'a bloody
hard hill to graze on'. Today he
says nothing about it, as though it's
only there for decoration.
In the evening the sky is orange and
pink. It lights up the
tree's scars and emphasises its shadow.
I like to go up there
when I need to think.
There often will be a dead sheep
carcass on the other side,
its body bloated. At the top
you can see 360 degrees around.
The layers of clouds
don't move and the distant electrical
posts stalk the sky.
Pine wind-breaks crawl like caterpillars.

Days run away.
One Tree Hill is still here and will be here when I return.

Betty Thompson

PUT OUR HOUSE IN ORDER
Malcolm Fraser

Our government has failed to lead us in acting with urgency and generosity on reconciliation.

We only have to look at the main differences in terms of life expectancy and health. Let me quote from a letter sent in 1997 by Dr Keith Wollard, then President of the AMA, and Professor Ian Ring of James Cook University, which was published in *The Weekend Australian*.

They wrote:

'In just three short decades, the health status of Maoris has improved dramatically. This is in stark contrast to the health of Indigenous Australians. In 1950, the life expectancy for Maori people was 15 years less than non-Maoris. By 1992 the gap had been cut to just five years. In contrast, Aboriginal people die 16 to 20 years younger than the rest of the population. Important factors in the improved health status of Maori people include: Maori control of health services; health service provision in a wider context of language, culture and social services; workforce development designed to close the training gap between Maoris and non-Maoris receiving the same level of funding as a non-Maori with similar health problems. Indigenous Australians receive a substantially lower level of health care services in many areas, despite being in greater need.'

Self-determination has always been a significant factor in improving the situation in New Zealand, as indeed it has in Canada. 'Self-determination' very largely means being able to have charge of their own life the way the rest of us can take charge of ours. So let's forget about any fears or concerns about that word and accept it as reasonable.

If the treatment of the original inhabitants of Australia, by the white settlers, represents the darkest hour in Australian history, the rejection of what many Australians would regard as justified criticism of Australian policies by international institutions, in a way that puts jingoistic nationalism over and above the concept and ideal of human rights, is a step into the past, which we should not have taken.

There have been some suggestions that reconciliation must become more and more a people's movement. In one sense people have responded to that by marching with their feet. But in another sense, it is wrong.

Issues of race are always the hardest to resolve, especially when the issue involves property. They are most unlikely to be resolved by the initiative of citizens alone, unless those citizens so hound their politicians that the politicians become frightened not to act. But that happens rarely.

50 000 people in Brisbane, 250 000 in Sydney, 55 000 in Adelaide and 20 000 in Hobart represents a good start, and governments should take note. This is an issue on which votes will change.

But it is the government that is informed, it is the government that is meant to have all the facts, it is the government that has resources, authority and power, it is the government whose files contain the evidence of the past that today we condemn. In a matter so critical to the future of society and the future of Australia, it is not reasonable to say the community must lead. The community and its actions are an important component, but it is the government that must be to the fore and persuade all Australians that we must act with greater expedition and with greater generosity. Government – if not this one, then another – will set the pace.

Malcolm Fraser was Prime Minister from 1975 to 1983. This is an edited extract of his Vincent Lingiari Memorial Lecture, 2000.

t guided by true lo

estination may nev

its direction is cons

love is to be stron

d to understand wh

eding on trust and

e will reveal a

DEATH REGISTERED IN NEW SOUTH WALES, AUS

No.	Date and place of death	Name and occupation	Sex and age	Cause of death Duration of last illness; medical attendant; when he last saw deceased	Name and occupation of father Name and maiden surname of mother

can

be c

nt a

and

is

mpas

ndrou

8 February 2003

Dear Diary,

Christina is my cousin as well as my sister!?

When she told me who her biological mother was – Therese Freedman – I knew straightaway the truth that had been kept buried and hidden from us for so long.

I was shocked. Therese would have been 17 and Albert would have been 22. He had just left Mum around that time, now I know why. He was cheating on Mum with her cousin Therese and when he found out Therese was pregnant, he left town to avoid the consequences.

Therese went to Melbourne to have the baby and gave Christina up for adoption. All these years, Mum, Dad and Great Aunty Betty have kept this dark secret.

Christina was the shame of this family. Well, I don't think she has anything to be ashamed about. She is still my sister, and cousin, and that's what makes our bond stronger. This secret was bound to come out sooner or later, and I'm not going to let Christina carry this burden.

Today I sent her this quote: 'Gnokan Danna Murra Kor-ki.'
'Give me your hand my friend and bridge the cultural gap.'

Adele

Love will
reveal a
wondrous
growth.
It is
eternal.

Dear Therese,

A heart guided by true love can do no wrong.
Its destination may never be certain,
But its direction is constant and sure.
To love is to be stronger and more perceptive
And to understand what is just and righteous,
Feeling on trust and compassion.
Love will reveal a wondrous growth.
It is eternal, never ceasing to exist,
Although hiding from those too self-absorbed to find it.

Albert Thompson
12 December 1987

28 February 2003

I cried at school today. It was so strange, actually. Two weeks ago, I wouldn't have cried. I wouldn't have cared or even noticed. In fact I probably would have said something quite like it myself. But today it made me cry. My teacher, Mr Miles, said to tell him, he'd sort it out. But I knew he wouldn't ever understand. You see this is what happened.

Jimmy Evans was having a fight with Scott, and Jimmy yelled out, 'Scott, you are as dirty as a stinking Abo, no you're worse than a stinking Abo.' And Scott yelled back, 'Nah, no one's WORSE than an Abo.' And then the fight was over and they all laughed, throwing their heads back and slapping their knees. They thought it was hysterical. Then, it hit me. A tightness around my ribs and shortness of breath in my lungs. I was Aboriginal. In the past I had heard people say those words – abos, coons and boongs. Words that should be banned from the English language. I wanted to go and yell at both of them, to tell them that they were racist pigs and say straight to their faces, 'Excuse me, but I'm Aboriginal, did you know?!'

But I didn't because, although I wanted them to know that they were racist pigs, I didn't want them to think that I was the worst type of person. They liked me. If I told them, I'm sure they wouldn't. Then the tears started as it set in. 'I'm the worst type there is.'

This day has been awful. No one could ever understand how much this has hurt me. I am beginning to understand Albert's anger over injustice.

I am the unloved, unwanted and constantly taunted. There is no one who cares enough to defend or protect me from hateful words.

Rachel

To my mother, whoever you are,

Anger wins the battle

The rage I feel is unbearable
It needs to escape and leave me
But how, or when will it go
I'm so sick of what they think of me
And who they judge me by
It seems I'm not my own person
But am living with earlier mistakes
That I have learnt not to make
I wish they could see me, as me

An argument makes things worse
But I can't get my point across
And the anger feeds inside me
Something that I cannot control
When will it strike, on who
Or will it just sit inside me
Driving me quietly insane
As everything I do and see
Reminds me too much of hate

It overrides everything I do
And causes my moods to change
Too quickly and abruptly
What should I expect from myself
But is it hate that I feel
Or just a raging anger
No matter what I do or say
They will not see me as myself
But judge me, punish me

I just wish that I could break through
The cage that you put me in
Throwing away the key
Trying to save me from the dangers
Of the outside world
But these dangers are everywhere
I know how to escape them
Can't you see this
I am not him

Albert Thompson

Dear Therese,

Hide Away

There's a place in my heart
That's yours alone
A part of my life
No one else can own
The tears in my eyes
I can hide away
But the pain in my heart
Will always stay

Christina

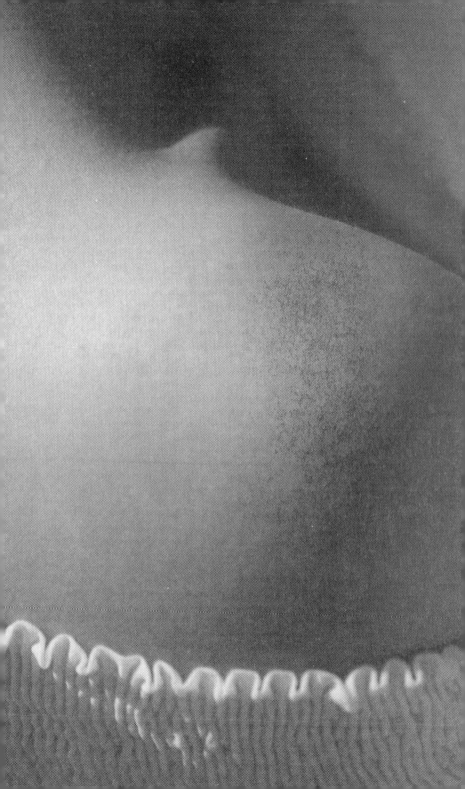

7 March 2003

Dear Adele,

I am starting to accept you can't change what has happened in the past but you can live to make a better future. The nightmares are going away and I no longer feel lonely or that everyone is deserting me. I don't have many friends or people I can trust. My new family are the most important people in my life. No one can take our connection away from us. I want to learn as much as possible about my people and culture and pass this on to my future children and their children. Our meeting has changed my life. I couldn't ever explain what I feel to my friends. Unless you've been though what we are going through, you couldn't have a clear understanding of what it feels like. We have an unspoken connection and I feel the support. You trust your own. We have to take this journey slowly and together. I want to meet Albert as soon as we can but I know this contact has to be done slowly because the emotions are so intense. We are all part of the story. We will go through a lot together and that will make us stronger and closer.

Aboriginal culture is extraordinary. It heals you.

In the past, I would often sit and daydream about the 'perfect life'...

INGREDIENTS OF LIFE

2 parents
2 sisters
A great deal of patience
1 cup of dreams
At least 2 tablespoons of education
1 house
Unlimited amount of friends
A cup of health
1 heart
1 mind
1 soul
Desired amount of personality
2 or 3 careers
1 litre of husbandry (your choice)
Extensive romantic nights
Up to 24 hours of excruciating labour pains
3 or 4 children
Hundreds of smelly nappies and sleepless nights
Tons of teenager-parent fights
A few proud moments
1 dash of old age
1 death
Unlimited amount of afterlife

Take two parents and mix together to create you, then add in the sisters for extra spice. Now add the patience and dreams as a starting point for life. Over a specific time period add education to build up a layer of knowledge. Pour in the house then, with a delicate hand, add the friends. With the cup of health, put in a pinch of heart, mind and soul, which are the most important ingredients, so be careful. The personality and careers must be mixed in well to work. After a few years, melt in the husband and the romantic nights. At this stage you are pregnant with nowhere to run. Pour in the labour pains and soon the children. Place the nappies, sleepless nights and teenager-parent fights into a round tin and cook for 18 years. For extra taste, add the proud moments and old age. Soon you will be dead and the afterlife will arrive, so allow time to let it cool. Serve with one funeral.

How predictable. Now my dream is different. It is not a predictable dream that conforms with non-Aboriginal culture. It is my dream.

Christina

14 March 2003

Dear Adele and Christina,

I read the scrapbook last night. It is so sad and I could not stop crying. I don't want to see you again. I don't feel like I am part of your family and it's not because I am the youngest. Everything about having an Aboriginal background is sad. I wish you had never contacted me nor that I had ever read this stupid scrapbook.

Who am I truly?

Who am I truly?
I know my name and what I've done,
But I want to know where I'm from.
My people, the land and culture.
Who and what are they?
Where do I belong?
I'm getting so confused,
I am a piece of a puzzle.
People try and put me into place,
But I am both white and black.
Wouldn't that come out grey?
If the pieces would just fit together,
I would find my place.
I would find my history then,
I would find out who I truly am.

Rachel

Of all the questions concerning the injustices experienced by the Aborigines after the dispossession, Aboriginal child removal - perhaps because it concerns a violation universally understood, the separation of mother and child - was the one which most deeply captured the national imagination. After the publication of 'Bringing Them Home' many Australians were astonished to discover what had happened so recently in their country's history and what they had previously failed to understand or even to see. This story had the power to change forever the way they saw their history.

PROFESSOR ROBERT MANNE
'IN DENIAL'
THE AUSTRALIAN
QUARTERLY ESSAY

No one denies that physical problems – health, housing, education, employment – are important to reconciliation. But reconciliation must be about more than living standards. It has to begin with an act of recognition – recognition that the European settlement of this continent, from which we have all drawn huge benefits, came at a terrible cost to Aboriginal Australians. This also requires acknowledgment that we failed to adequately recognise what was done and, with some noble exceptions, to make the most basic human response and enter into the hearts and minds of Indigenous Australians. We failed to ask: 'How would this feel if this were done to me?'

I am optimistic about the future because I think hearts are opening. We see it in powerful, spontaneous support for reconciliation right across the Australian community. We see it too, in the determination of writers like Robert Manne never again to let the distortions and untruths stand unchallenged.

This is an edited extract of former Prime Minister Paul Keating's address to launch Robert Manne's Quarterly Essay.

16 March 2003

Dear Great Aunty Betty,

After your letter I met with Christina and Rachel and we decided to put together a scrapbook for Albert. This is our life story in print. Although the scrapbook is full of sad stories and anger, we feel that we understand more about who Albert really is – a sensitive and creative man who is unable to form relationships because of the loss of his family when he was a little boy.

I think it is all about understanding and forgiveness. These problems are all-consuming. We will only be at peace when we are prepared to put our problems behind us, forgive and make a fresh start. I once read something about how to forgive someone. Just imagine yourself in a beautiful place. In the distance, imagine the person slowly walking towards you. When the person is within eye contact, perform a gesture of your choice, which to you symbolises forgiveness. Gently release your adversary. Sit still to feel your peace. I have forgiven Albert now. I would like to help others understand how to forgive. I would like to contribute.

But the whole thing has upset Rachel. She is too scared to go outside her comfort zone. I finally feel I belong somewhere but I understand it is all too painful for Rachel. Going through all this makes me very sensitive to her pain. Her sheltered world has been turned upside down.

When we were putting together our experiences of racism, it made us feel that true reconciliation is a long way away. How do you find the strength to face the future when the struggle is so hard? If our story could make just one person understand, it would be worth it.

We are not sure what to do or if we should even write to Albert. Please give us some advice. What would you do if this happened to you?

Adele

25 March 2003

Dear Adele, Christina and Rachel,

You have learnt the real secret. The real secret is the power of understanding and forgiveness to overcome anger and sadness.

The words of Albert's poems have deep meaning but they are not all sad. Your father loves you and he also expresses this in his poetry.

Standing in the forest,
Held up by the vines,
Surrounded by the ferns
Is this little shack of mine,

The roof is leaky
And the rain drips in,
But what can you expect
From the rusty old tin.

It slants to the right
And the squeaks come from the door,
It has one broken window
And a stained dirty floor.

But on the windy nights
When the wind whips through the wall,
And my hut is shivering,
It could easily fall.

The memories of my daughters
I wrap around me tight,
And suddenly I'm safe and warm,
I know everything will be all right.

Your scrapbook expresses your anger, courage, honesty and sensitivity to Albert's suffering. You are opening your hearts to a new understanding – the importance of feeling connected to family and community, the need to persevere through difficulties and to develop optimism about the future by retelling the story of the past. By being big enough to ask the question: 'How would this feel if this were done to me?' you have demonstrated the power of understanding.

Many people were too afraid to face the truth of the 'Bringing Them Home' report because it had the power to rewrite Australian history and it raised the ugly issue of compensation. It was government policy to breed out black to eradicate the 'Aboriginal problem' and make us easier to manage. It was only in 1967 that Aboriginal people became entitled to services by being acknowledged for the first time as Australian citizens. A lot of people don't realise how recent this history is and how the effects have flowed on to the younger generations of Aboriginal people today.

The government keeps putting us in the too-hard basket but there are some glaringly obvious things that can be done to improve things for our people. Attendance at school is one huge area. If we improve education, we improve our opportunities for employment and to influence the wider community. Our young people would stay at school if the government would take leadership on this issue and clamp down on racism. The silence of good people allows discrimination and racism.

Our people are taking a stand. We have strong role models. We are trying to make a better future for our people. And I am also optimistic about the future because you are beginning to understand. I feel your loss. Being part of our community will ease your pain. Our community is concerned about your emotional and spiritual wellbeing. You will learn your culture by talking and listening, not necessarily by art, language and skin. Once you learn your culture you will find what is missing – the secret of the spiritual side.

I can understand Rachel's feelings. She doesn't know where she belongs or who she is. She is not part of black or white society but she has been brought up with non-Aboriginal thinking and different values from the materialistic world. A lot of young people like this just can't adjust. They don't know their living culture or family. I say to these people: you don't have to prove anything, but don't forget who you are and just accept who you are.

Please send Albert the scrapbook. He, of all people, will understand your anger and your sadness. I know he will write back and everything will be all right.

With much love,
Great Aunty Betty

What would you do if this happened to you?

Write to Dr Jason Fitzgerald, Adele, Christina and Rachel.

Send a letter or poem via the website:
users.pipeline.com.au/lrowe

Your contribution might be published in the next book.

Joleen Ryan is currently studying for a Bachelor of Social Work at Deakin University and is a member of the National Indigenous Youth Leadership Group and the Victorian Family Violence Taskforce.

Julia Torpey is an Arts student at the University of Melbourne and enjoys music, swimming at the beach and going out with friends. She sings like an angel.

Megan Torpey has just returned from Kent in the UK where she was working as a teacher's aide. She is now studying first-year Arts at the University of Melbourne and enjoys living in the city and playing softball.

Tegan Watson is currently undertaking a Certificate of Business Administration at Wathaurong Aboriginal Cooperative. She loves bushwalking!

Zac Brennan is currently undertaking an Arts Degree at the University of Melbourne while managing a well-known restaurant in Fitzroy. His mind is a 'tangle of fantastic ideas'. In 2001 he coauthored the book *girl_X recreated* with Leanne and Shayne.

Dr Leanne Rowe is a general practitioner and was awarded 'Best Individual Contribution to Health Care in Australia' by the Australian Medical Association for her work with young people. Her other positions include Chairman of the Royal College of General Practitioners (Vic).

Shayne Lacy studied architecure, directs a graphic design studio, and is currently undertaking a degree in linguistics while learning a few foreign languages.

Afterword

It will always be the greatest honour of my career that the Wathaurong Aboriginal Cooperative allowed me to work with their young people for the last two years to produce *Urgent* to open the hearts of non-Aboriginal people.

A core group of teenagers, Joleen Ryan, Megan Torpey, Julia Torpey, Tegan Watson and Zac Brennan, wrote the story and encouraged over 30 other young Aboriginal and non-Aboriginal people to contribute personal accounts of their lives as well as poetry, artwork and photography. The characters in the book are fictional but the stories are true. The process of putting the book together was as important as the final product. We consulted widely with youth groups, schools and through the website **users.pipeline.com.au/lrowe**. Mrs Lyn McInnes, Chair of Wathaurong Aboriginal Cooperative and board member of the National Aboriginal Community Controlled Health Organisations Board was a great supporter of the project, as were the Wathaurong staff. Shayne Lacy, studio director of mspace, engaged young people in the design of the book. The Reach Foundation auspiced the funding for the community consultation from the Stronger Families and Communities Strategy of the Commonwealth Department of Family and Community Services. Clockwork Young People's Health Service also supported the project.

We are grateful to the team of people who believed in the manuscript in its early stages including Kerry McCarthy, Kathy Travis (Gordon TAFE), Sharon Stynes, Jim Stynes, Yelda Adal (The Reach Foundation), Jo Murray (Australian Medical Association), David Bennett (Centre for the Advancement of Adolescent Health), Ian Hickie (beyond blue), Scott Hocknull (Young Australian of the Year 2002), Keryn Negri, Leonie Saundry, Catherine Bell (Office for Youth) and Julie Gainey (The Geelong College). A very big thank you is extended to Mr Bruce Pascoe, who gave crucial editorial advice. The book was made possible by Linsay Knight and Eva Mills from Random House. We are also indebted to The Hon. Malcolm Fraser, The Hon. Paul Keating, Professor Robert Manne,

Mr George Megalogenis and Mr Ron Tandberg for permission to include their work.

Why did we write the book? I wrote Dr Jason Fitzgerald's letter based on my experience as a general practitioner working in a community-controlled Aboriginal Health Service in Far North Queensland nearly 10 years ago. Since that time, health statistics have not changed significantly and Aboriginal people continue to have 20 years less life expectancy than non-Aboriginal people. I have met many young Aboriginal people who lose their parents prematurely and are devastated and disadvantaged by grief. A significant number drop out of school because of experiences of loss and injustice. Less than 30% of Aboriginal students complete Year 12.

Urgent is aimed at students to stimulate discussion of the issues and to increase their understanding and intolerance of racism. As Mrs Lyn McInnes said: 'There are some glaringly obvious things the government could do to help our people. Aboriginal communities need to be able to employ their own people to support students through difficult times to keep them at school from Prep to Year 12. This would make a great difference.'

Our book demands an answer to the question: What would you do if this happened to you? Young Aboriginal and non-Aboriginal people are encouraged to answer the question and to contribute to the sequel through the website **users.pipeline.com.au/ lrowe**. The website also provides resources for teachers to assist them to introduce the book into the school curriculum.

When I ask the question and I try to put myself in the shoes of Adele, Christina or Rachel, I know I would feel irreparably hurt if Dr Jason Fitzgerald sent a formal letter of regret, a reassurance about practical reconciliation or questioned the existence of a Stolen Generation. It is my hope that Jason's reply will begin with the words: I am deeply, deeply sorry...

Dr Leanne Rowe

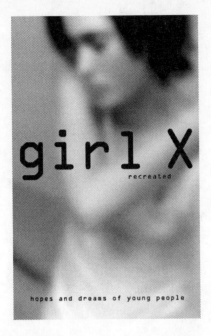

girl X recreated is the intriguing, beautifully illustrated diary of an imaginary Year 12 student. Capturing her feelings on commitment, friendship, family, depression, drugs, racism, war and the future in uncertain times, it also expresses the courage and, at times, despair of the young people who created this extraordinary character - a powerful message of hope to young people like themselves.